IMAGES
of England

SOUTH YORKSHIRE
COLLIERIES

John Goodchild, M. Univ

For my friend Arthur Clayton

IMAGES
of England

SOUTH YORKSHIRE
COLLIERIES

John Goodchild, M. Univ

TEMPUS

First published 2001
Copyright © John Goodchild, 2001

Tempus Publishing Limited
The Mill, Brimscombe Port,
Stroud, Gloucestershire, GL5 2QG
www.tempus-publishing.com

ISBN 0 7524 2148 4

Typesetting and origination by
Tempus Publishing Limited
Printed in Great Britain by
Midway Colour Print, Wiltshire

The images used in this book are from the collections in the author's Local History Study Centre at Wakefield.

Contents

Introduction

The purpose behind the working of any colliery was to make a profit. Whether the colliery was worked by an individual, a partnership, a limited liability company, even by a co-operative, a colliery was a business first and foremost. There were a few exceptions, for example a medieval colliery often worked to supply a monastic house, or one was worked informally as a surface working by men and women during a strike. Almost always though, profit was the motive, and when the coal proved uneconomic when sunk to, was exhausted or in some other way uneconomic to work, by flooding or fire for example, the colliery was closed.

The task of the historian of coal mining is essentially to identify the factors which, in combination, allowed the development of the coal resources of an area or of a particular concern. Sometimes the historian will be faced with a wealth of information, but not always. What information can be found that was directly produced by the coal mining entrepreneurs themselves is often scattered and incomplete, and will have to be supplemented with illustrations, maps, newspaper and journal references, government publications, union and master's association records, local histories, trade directories, etc, as well as a study of the physical remains surviving and even – if possible – by the recording of personal recollections. All of these methods were utilised in preparing this present account of the coal mining industry in South Yorkshire.

The principal factors governing the development and successful operation of any colliery were as follows:

1. The coal itself: its quality, depth, thickness, faulting, wetness
2. The availability of markets
3. Accessible transport facilities, especially water and rail
4. The availability of investment capital
5. The use of technical expertise
6. The abilities of partners and employees
7. The availability of leaseable or purchasable coal and wayleaves
8. Timing in regard to growing demands for coal
9. Plain luck

This volume examines some of these matters.

Coal has been worked and used in the West Riding of Yorkshire since the Roman occupation at least. This continued despite the ready availability of timber as fuel until the sixteenth and seventeenth centuries, as evidenced by the numerous documentary references to the working of coal in the area from the thirteenth century. So, from medieval times at least, this coal was certainly used in part for iron working purposes. Other more diverse industrial purposes followed such as glass making, brick making, lime burning, pottery manufacture and coke making, while coal, of course, continued to be used for domestic heating and latterly too for the production of steel and for gas manufacture.

The South Yorkshire coalfield is, geologically speaking, a portion of the large Yorkshire and Midlands coalfield extending from an artificial northern boundary running through Woolley and from the northern extremity of the exposure of the thick Barnsley seam of coal, southwards to the county boundary with Derbyshire and Nottinghamshire. Westwards, it extends into the hill country above Sheffield, and eastwards the exposed coalfield's boundary runs in a roughly north to south line through Conisborough on the river Don. Further east, coal only began to be worked from the mid-nineteenth century and it was not until 1905 that there was a major expansion into the Doncaster area, east of the Magnesian limestone ridge, with pits ultimately located as far east as Thorne.

A variety of minerals were worked alongside coal or in association with it: ironstone, clay, fire-resistant ganister and a small amount of lead. Tar and coke were by-products from the eighteenth century and various chemicals a nineteenth century venture. In the latter part of the nineteenth century some collieries were taken over by steel making concerns, just as earlier iron making businesses had owned collieries and ironstone pits.

As in the sister West Yorkshire coalfield to the north, the story of coal mining in South Yorkshire may be divided into three distinct periods. The first of these lasted until the onset of water transport as the most economical form of transport and enabled industry to open up wider markets, extending principally to the Ouse, Humber and Trent basins. The second dates from the 1740s, when the Don Navigation opened into the coalfield, followed by the opening of water routes constructed both within the coalfield area itself and others connecting with it, to 1819 when the short Sheffield Canal from Tinsley was opened. The waterway system was later to be improved in route and the size of vessels taken, and also significantly extended, particularly in relation to coal carriage, with the opening of the New Junction Canal in 1905, which connected the Don Navigation and its feeder waterways with the Port of Goole. Waterway transport continued to carry coal alongside the new railways, despite the physical collapse of some coal carrying canals in South Yorkshire as a result of subsidence occasioned by coal extraction. Much of the system remains in use today, despite the collapse of the local coal mining industry.

The large-scale sale of coal from Yorkshire in the London markets was a development commencing in the 1850s, facilitated by the opening of the Great Northern Railway, but attempts to break into that market had been previously made. In the days of long distance carriage of coal solely by waterways, the collieries of the Great Northern coalfield – essentially of the valleys of the Tyne, Wear and Tees – had an advantage in that their carriage in large vessels from close to the pits resulted in cheaper sale prices in London. Coal brought from far inland on the growing system of Yorkshire waterways was either sent onwards in larger vessels from Hull, or had to go all the way in small, river-navigation sized vessels without transshipment, with obvious effects on the price. In addition, the Yorkshire coals had to compete in a London market which had been used to the particular quality of northern coals since medieval times, while Yorkshire coals had to initiate sales in the face of a prejudice against them.

Perhaps the earliest attempt to break into this rich London market was made in the late 1780s when the great canal engineer William Jessop and his partner sent 'a ship load of Coals' to London 'as an experiment, however, 'it did not answer', as Jessop believed, on account of the inferiority of the (Mirfield area) coal. Small quantities of coal were exported from Hull in 1790 to 1794, and in 1800 it was reported that coals had been sent to London some time ago, but none recently, and no Yorkshire coals had been received in the Port of London from January 1798 to March 1800.

However, Yorkshire coals were quoted on the London Coal Exchange by 1802, although the supply was obviously irregular. Leaving aside the problem as to whether Brandling and Brandling Main coals were both from Tyneside, the Yorkshire coals quoted were:

Wentworth	South Yorkshire	once only, in 5.1802
Dewsbury Main	West Yorkshire	thrice, in June 1802
Stanley Main	–	once only, in June 1802
Allerton	–	no prices quoted
Flockton	–	–
Methley Park	–	–

The Silkstone coals are said to have been tried on the London market in 1805, but at a loss, and then again from 1828, albeit in small quantities. To encourage the distant coal markets, to which coal was carried in one bottom in seagoing boats known as 'Billy Boys', the bridges on the Wakefield to Barnsley and Cawthorne canal (the Barnsley Canal) were raised in height in 1828 to allow the passage of these vessels, which rode high when empty.

In the late 1820s Yorkshire exports of coal to London averaged 25,000 tons a year and by 1837 only 16,000 tons, but the figure rose in 1840 to 60,000. Exports of coal from Hull rose slowly too – from 7,500 tons in 1833, but by 1860 they totalled 159,000 tons, while coal exports from Goole rose from 6,000 tons in 1851 to 19,000 in 1859, and at Grimsby in those same years from a mere 4,000 tons to 103,000.

The British – and especially English – railway was born out of the coal industry's need for large-scale, economic transportation, a need that was to spread world-wide. While South Yorkshire did not witness the 'firsts' in regards to an Act of Parliament, the first public railway and railway company or the first successful steam locomotion, there was an early railway at Sheffield in 1722-1723. Also railways were built to the newly-navigable river Don in the 1740s and by 1766 the Fentons' Greasborough waggonway used rails topped with iron strips. At Rawmarsh adjoining the Don, the Enclosure Act of 1774 refers to a railway route already staked out across a common about to be enclosed, and ultimately there were several dozen miles of colliery (and ironstone pit) railways in South Yorkshire. At Elsecar, an early industrial loco-motive was in use by 1840, while others used inclined planes and horse and bullock traction. John Curr, who introduced the L-section rail, worked at Sheffield and introduced his plates, initially underground, in 1787; their use soon spread for use, albeit comparatively briefly, on surface railways.

However, it was the steam-powered railways which broadened the coal markets of South Yorkshire in both geographic and output terms. The short Sheffield & Rotherham Railway had been opened in 1838, and the North Midland Railway, which passed through the eastern part of the exposed coalfield, had first connected the area with London and the south of England from 1840, but marketing difficulties prevented the South (and indeed West) Yorkshire coals entering these markets in quantity prior to the opening of the Great Northern Railway's line from Askern and Doncaster to London in 1850 and the independent feeder railway companies' reaching into the heart of the coalfield.

Thereafter many new collieries were sunk, with large capital outlay and financed utilising the new limited liability facilities to raise the necessary money. Some of these ventures had open associations with the railway companies but there were many who hid such partnerships. This third period of development in the coalfield of South Yorkshire can be said, despite the arrival of the motor lorry, to have survived until today.

Within the area of the South Yorkshire coalfield some of the coal resources lay under land owned by small freeholders, a factor which could cause legal difficulties – as happened at Royston with the obtaining of coal leases for Monckton Main Colliery in the 1870s.

Other areas were owned by large landowners, many of whom grew rich from the mineral resources of their land, and, thus aided, were able to remain in occupation of their estates until modern times

It was claimed in the 1890s that only one eighth of the coal forming the South Yorkshire Coalfield was actually worked by the owners of the coal. The successive Earls Fitzwilliam, of the palatial mansion Wentworth Woodhouse, were the most prominent in output, and indeed in their social provision for their workforce, at their collieries at Elsecar and Stubbin.

But the opening up of any new colliery demanded not only capital but technical expertise as well – administrators, experienced salesmen, managers, overmen and, of course, workmen. A large colliery in the area at the end of the nineteenth century was one which produced 1,500 tons of coal a day, employing around 1,000 men and boys (children and women had been forbidden to work underground from 1842). For such a colliery, $1\frac{1}{2}$ tons a day per man was the norm.

Of course, by the railway period, coal mining was an ancient industry, and many seams were nearing exhaustion, especially the less deep seams of the better quality, thicker coal, and so deeper and more expensive sinkings had to made. Often these were made in areas where there was no knowledge of the quality of the seam it was proposed to work and an imperfect knowledge of the geological faulting which could prove financially catastrophic.

The Geological Survey was beginning its important work locally by the 1860s, and there was already interest in matters geological in the area, but risk was endemic in the coal industry: fortunes were there to be made, but many failed in their endeavours. Within the old areas of coal working there were the additional dangers of unknown and unmapped old workings, usually water filled, and explosions of gas which were to bring the South Yorkshire coalfield to international attention when they occurred at Lundhill, the Oaks, Edmunds Main and Swaithe Main to name but a few. Coal mining was a business with risks to the pocket and the person; it was a struggle between man and man, but also between man and nature.

The availability of local foundries with engineering skills was essential to coal mining development from the end of the eighteenth. Some large colliery concerns ultimately opened their own workshops and were able to deal with such complexities as the building of winding engines, locomotives and other major works, as well as with repairs and less complex engineering ventures, but for initial plant, outside firms had to be relied upon. The writer has recently acquired the records of the engineering firm of Bradley & Craven on the outskirts of Wakefield, founded in 1843 and with detailed records surviving from 1849 – they made winding drums, headgear pullies, iron cages, weighing machines, winding engines and pumping machinery for numerous collieries. For the then new Woolley Colliery they supplied pumping machinery in 1856 and a new engine beam in 1860. In 1859 they built a pair of large, 60hp horizontal winding engines for the new Darfield Main Colliery and in 1863 a pair of 100hp horizontal, high-pressure steam winding engines for the Denaby Coal Co. Bradley & Craven were of course not the only working foundry in the area, although perhaps the survival of their records is unusual.

The prescribed length of this essay does not allow us to deal with the minutiae of mining development in South Yorkshire, although some detail is included in the commentary upon the illustrations in this book. Suffice it to say here that as time passed, shafts deepened, improved machinery was introduced, better trained staff were available, new methods of working coal – including underground machinery and coal-cutting machines – came into use. Better quality housing for the men and their families, including provision of schools and chapels, was introduced, along with trade unionism to protect the rights of the men and boys. New markets for South Yorkshire coal were found – even if on occasion this involved the 'theft' of the name Wallsend from Tyneside – and international markets were developed, including the use of local coal for powering steamships which fought or traded in distant waters.

Ultimately, after long battles fought by the men and by the politicians, the coal resources were nationalised in 1938 and the coal industry itself in 1947, save a few small mines, of which

Flacks of Clayton West remains the oldest and best-known today. The Selby area coalfield was to be developed in the time of the National Coal Board, but demands for coal changed, less valuable seams were necessarily worked, foreign coal was imported cheaply, the domestic and gas coal markets disappeared, and political prejudices were active. Today, there remain in South Yorkshire only the large Maltby Main, Hatfield and Rossington collieries and all three are privately owned.

Something of the enormous growth of the Yorkshire coalfields – that of South Yorkshire is not specified alone – may be gained for much of the period covered by the illustrations in this books by the following table:

Year	Output of Coal (tons)	Number of Employees
1870	11,545,400	36,500
1880	17,468,536	60,474
1890	22,335,110	76,776
1900	28,243,507	100,803
1906	32,547,905	115,508

The author has chosen to illustrate only some of the South Yorkshire collieries of which he has images, and to some of these is attached a more lengthy description than to others, as the pictures used give more insight into aspects of the coalfield and its associated workers' and owners' lives and concerns.

The reader might usefully also refer to the writer's companion volume on the West Yorkshire coalfields published by Tempus in 2000.

Following page:
Barrow Colliery at the end of the nineteenth century: a large South Yorkshire colliery at work. Sinking began in June 1873, just to the south of Barnsley, by the Barrow (in Furness) Haematite Steel Co. Ltd which claimed to be the largest producer of Bessemer steel in the world. It was intended to provide a supply of coking and other coal for the steelwork's use. The Silkstone – a caking coal – was reached in January 1876 and was approximately 5ft in thickness, at 470 yards. The colliery, with its coke ovens and by-product works, was bought in 1932 by the new Barrow Barnsley Main Co. whose predecessor already owned Barnsley Main Colliery (from 1899) and had acquired Thorncliffe Coal Distillation Ltd in 1925 and Monk Bretton Colliery in 1939.

By 1939 the company employed 4,560 men and boys at Barrow and Barnsley Main collieries, with an output of some 1.3 million tons of coal – and Monk Bretton was to provide even more.

Barnsley Main closed in 1966, Monk Bretton in 1968, and Barrow in 1985.

Setting the Scene

South Elmsall, Moorthorpe and District Distress Fund.

REPORT AND BALANCE SHEET,
APRIL to JULY, 1921.

Ladies and Gentlemen,

In presenting the closing Balance Sheet of the above Fund the Committee take this opportunity of thanking all subscribers, both for contributions in cash and in goods and for their very generous and continuous help.

The fund was commenced on the 24th April, 1921, being first considered by the South Elmsall Tradesmen's Association for the purpose of feeding the children during the dispute. From the first meeting however, an amalgamation of all parties in South Elmsall interested in the feeding of children took place, and the fund was launched into existence and called the South Elmsall, Moorthorpe and District Distress Fund.

The sum of £1474 8s. 2d. has been collected and disbursed amongst the women and children of the district in milk, soup, etc. In the distribution of this, 1,103 2-lb loaves, 71,120 milk buns, 9 tons potatoes, 161 stones carrots, 168 stones peas, 140 stones onions, 6,600 lbs. meat, 3,200 gallons new milk, 260 gallons skimmed milk and 350 lbs. oatmeal have been used. 49,083 soup dinners have been given to children between the ages of 3 and 14, in addition to 2,980 fish dinners and 5,500 dry rations. Messrs, Fenton, Clewes, Wormald and Flavell fried and distributed the fish dinners from their shops, assisted by the kitchen cooks. In additon Mr. Murgatroyd gave fish dinners on two occasions to a large number of children.

From April 29th to July 2nd about 800 tickets were issued to necessitous cases. Under this heading came maternity cases, bottle fed babies, delicate children, cases of illness, patients attending the Dispensary, Hospitals, etc., milk, eggs, oxo, pearl barley, cocoa, and oatmeal were distributed for these purposes at the Salvation Army Hall, which was kindly lent for the occasion. The milk dealers supplied and distributed 1 gill of milk per head per day for six days in each week to children under 3 years of age, charging only the wholesale price to the Committee.

For the last week of the Relief the Committee distributed 3,353 vouchers for food at the rate of 1/8 per head, amounting to the sum of £279 8s. 4d.

The Frickley Colliery Co. Ltd., in addition to a liberal weekly contribution towards the kitchens, very kindly lent to the Committee cooking coppers for the use of the kitchens erected in the Chequers yard, and also fuel for the fires. Special thanks are due to Messrs. Graham & Daft, who during the whole existence of the fund used their large copper and personally assisted in the making of 100 gallons of soup 4 days per week.

Thanks are due also to Mr. Hutton of the Chequers Hotel, who placed his back premises at the services of the Committee for the purpose of making and distributing the soup, buns, etc., and also for the use of his Market Hall in which the Committee meetings were held.

The Committee wish to thank those who kindly lent their horses and carts for the purpose of conveying the goods to the cooking centres. Special mention should be made of the small army of men who have rendered such valuable service in the cooking and conveying of goods at the kitchens, and also those who carried out the registration and the distribution of tickets. This has entailed a considerable amount of hard work and the Committee and the general public are much indebted to these willing workers for their services.

In conclusion therefore, the Committee again thank all who have assisted in this movement, subscribers of monies and goods, loans of vehicles, utensils, premises, and everyone who has assisted in the administration of the fund in any capacity.

On behalf of the Committee,
A. SMITH, President,
T. GRAHAM, Treasurer,
W. S. WALTON, } Hon. Secs.
T. WATSON, }

Geo. F. Brook, Ltd., The Printing Office, South Elmsall.

Carlton Main Colliery at Carlton near Barnsley was established in 1872. In 1900 its owners bought out the new Grimethorpe Colliery, then sank Frickley Colliery, bought out the Hodroyd Coal Co. and made further developments in South Yorkshire before buying Hatfield Main Colliery in 1927 and expanding into North Wales and other fields closely associated with working coal. Its Report and Balance Sheet here shows a recommended dividend of 10%. In the years 1915 to 1918, it had paid at 50% per annum, and immediately before Nationalisation in 1945 and 1946, at 12%.

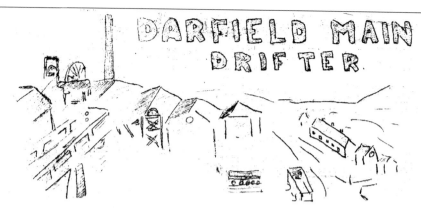

DARFIELD MAIN DRIFTER

Published by the Wombwell Communist Group.

1 9 2 9

WHAT WILL IT BRING FOR THE MINERS ?

No miner will regret the passing of 1928. It was a year of low wages, unemployment, unsafe working conditions, "Peace in Industry", Union splitting, and charity. Has 1929 anything better to offer ?

THE ORDER OF THE DAY

It seems that more unemployment, lower wages, and disqualification from benefit of unemployed men are to be the order of the day. Transference and emigration are offered as the substitute for work and wages.

CHARITY - OR STRENGTH TO FIGHT.

Shall the miners accept with bowed heads what the Bosses care to give them? Charity must end. Class aid must take its place. The only solution of permanent value will come from the organised strength of the working class.

CONDITIONS MAKE COMMUNISTS.

Mass poverty and suffering is making for political clarity. Thousands are realising that Capitalism is the cause of their misery, and that the misery will only be ended when Capitalism is ended.

LEADERS WHO WON'T LEAD

The Trade Union Movement has, in recent years played a cowards part in the Workers struggles. Comfort-ably situated Bureaucrats prefer industrial peace talks, surrendering their men's conditions to militant struggles. They talk of reorganising Capitalism but refuse to reorganise their own Unions. To save the Unions the Smith's and the Jones's must go.

SAVE THE UNION COMMITTEES

Militant workers must work and fight to save the Union for a policy of CLASS STRUGGLE instead of CLASS CUDDLE. Committees are being established throughout the country to demand a RANK and FILE BALLOT on the following issues: -

1. For or against Mondism.

2. For or against the disruption of the Scottish Unions.

3. For or against A.J.Cook as secretary

4. For or against Herbert Smith as President.

5. For or against ONE MINEWORKERS UNION.

Get in touch with the local Save the Union Movement through T. Mullins, 38, Knollbeck Avenue, Brampton, Wombwell. The only hope of the future is the building of militant Trade Unions and a Mass Communist Party.

The industrial relations in many collieries – but not all – were poor and increasingly politicised. Here is the Wombwell Communist Group's Darfield Main Colliery news-sheet from 1929.

RULES

OF THE

Primrose Main Colliery

WORKMEN'S

SICK & ACCIDENT

SOCIETY.

Barnsley:

R. E. GRIFFITHS, PRINTER AND LITHOGRAPHER, CHURCH STREET,

1905.

Primrose Main Colliery, on the outskirts of Barnsley, like some – but not all – collieries, had its own internal self-insurance society, to provide modest financial benefits in cases of illness and accident. A drift mine, Primrose Main was worked intermittently by a succession of owners from 1885 to the 1920s.

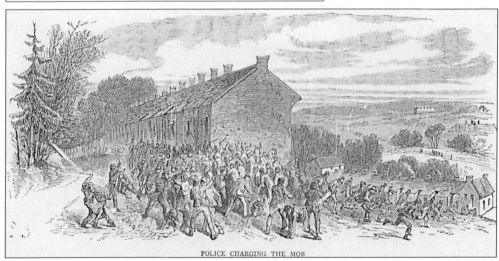

POLICE CHARGING THE MOB

Colliers' housing, probably of Newton, Chambers & Co., the iron, coal and ironstone producing company based on Chapeltown, at the time of the riots of 1870.

Colliery disasters were tragically not uncommon and often severe in South Yorkshire. They destroyed both lives and property. 189 lives were lost at the Lund Hill explosions in 1857. The Barnsley Bed coal was particularly liable to outbursts of explosive gas and this was the seam most sought after during most of the nineteenth century.

THE LUND HILL COLLIERY EXPLOSION : MOUTH OF THE DOWNCAST SHAFT.

BARNSLEY

PIT PONY & HORSE SHOW.

⇢✳ PRIZES. ✳⇠

COMPETITION 1.

The best Horse 14 hands or over.—1st Prize, £3 ; 2nd, £2 ; 3rd, £1.

The best Pony 12 hands and under 14.—1st Prize, £3 ; 2nd, £2 ; 3rd, £1.

The best Pony under 12 hands.—1st Prize, £3 ; 2nd, £2 ; 3rd, £1.

COMPETITION 2.

The best Horse or Pony certified to have worked in a Pit more than six years.—1st Prize, £3 ; 2nd, £2 ; 3rd, £1.

The best Horse or Pony certified to have worked in a Pit more than ten years.—First Prize, £3 ; 2nd, £2 ; 3rd, £1.

The Horse or Pony that has been working in a Pit the longest period.— 1st Prize, £3 ; 2nd, £2 ; 3rd, £1.

COMPETITION 3.

A group of Horses or Ponies.

In a Colliery where more than 50 Horses and Ponies are employed, six animals must be shewn.

In a Colliery where there are less than 50 and more than 30 Horses and Ponies employed, four animals must be shewn.

In a Colliery where less than 30 Horses and Ponies are employed, two animals must be shewn.

Half the animals must be selected by the Proprietors and half by the Committee by lot (see Rules).

1st Prize, £5 ; 2nd, £3 ; 3rd, £2.

COMPETITION 4.

There will also be a Prize awarded to the Pit which exhibits their animals in the best condition in the Pit.

Some one or two persons will be chosen by the Committee, who will during the months of June and July visit each Pit competing, at a time convenient to the Manager, but without notice as to the particular day.

On such visit every animal in the Pit must be shewn.

1st Prize, £5 ; 2nd, £3 ; 3rd, £2.

No entry fee is chargeable for the last competition. In all other classes 1s. entry fee for each animal must be paid, and from this fund refreshments will be provided for the persons in charge of the animals.

The Prizes will be distributed among the Drivers and Horse-keepers.

No person but the Judges and the person or persons having charge of the animals will be allowed in the Show-Ring on any pretext, unless asked to come in by the Judges.

Happier days. The Barnsley Pit Pony and Horse Show and its competitions, probably a later nineteenth century poster.

One

Before the Railway Age

A seventeenth century South Yorkshire colliery. This lease of coal at South Hiendley from 1662 was probably of the Shafton seam, 4ft 6in to 5ft in thickness (with dirt partings). The lease was to the owner of the nearby Hodroyd Hall. It alludes to 'All those Coles [sic]' under $1\frac{1}{2}$ acres in the Nether Field, sold for ninety-nine years for a modest £3 and was probably part of a larger worked area. Reference is made to the old sough, or underground channel, to the sough and to the road to the coalpit. Powers were granted for free entry for wains, carts, horses and carriages, to sink for and get coal and to dam, sough and set gins, for damages to be paid as a result of coal working, and for pits to be filled and ploughed over when finished.

This was apparently a typical rural colliery of the pre-waterway period, serving local agricultural communities' needs.

Coal was worked in the upland Penistone area in antiquity and continued to the twentieth century; Bullhouse Colliery last produced coal in 1963. Hinchliffe Bros are reputed to have worked twenty-four shafts at a depth of forty yards using underground scoops running on willow sticks and carrying coal twelve scoops to the ton by 1861. They were farmers who seem to have gone into coal mining. In 1903, J. Hinchliffe & Co.'s Bullhouse Colliery employed twenty-four, their Handbank nine, and Crow Edge eighteen. Bullhouse produced coal and fireclay. John and Herbert Hinchliffe were sufficiently rich to pay £5,500 for Bullhouse Hall and colliery and 150 acres of land at the estate sale of 1904, and further land for £2,700.

Here at Carlecotes, lying between Penistone and Holmfirth, ancient workings were recorded on film during opencast working in 1939.

The successive Earls Fitzwilliam and their predecessors owned 18,000 acres of mineral bearing land in South Yorkshire, opened up to wide sales by the completion of the Don Navigation to Tinsley in 1751.

In 1757 a lease of estate coal at Elsecar was signed, in 1757 one of Greasborough area coal and in 1835 one of Rawmarsh area coal. Water transport was improved for the estate by the opening of the Greasborough Canal in c.1780 and then by the opening of the Elsecar branch of the Dearne & Dove Canal in 1798. In preparation for this opening the Earl developed a new colliery at Elsecar in his own lands which involved new shafts, a water level, a large steam pumping engine, colliers' housing. Later additions included a church, schools, more houses, a lodging house, opened in 1853 for twenty-two men, a Market Hall opened in 1870, central workshops opened in 1850 and blast furnaces and ironworks at Elsecar and nearby Milton.

The arrival of steam railways resulted in increased sales: the Great Northern Railway purchased 800,000 tons of coal for resale in 1857 – it was prevented from coal dealing in 1859 – and in 1853 40% of Fitzwilliam coal was sold to the Great Northern. By the 1870s Fitzwilliam coal was on the British Admiralty's list of steam-raising coals and was being shipped at Hull, Grimsby, London, Goole, New Holland, Kings Lynn, Keadby and Liverpool.

The ultimate near exhaustion of the workable Barnsley Bed coal led to Fitzwilliam's sinking of a new colliery at Elsecar to work the Parkgate seam at 350 yards, completed in 1908, and the sinking of New – as opposed to the Old – Stubbin Colliery in 1913-1915. They closed in 1985 and 1978 respectively.

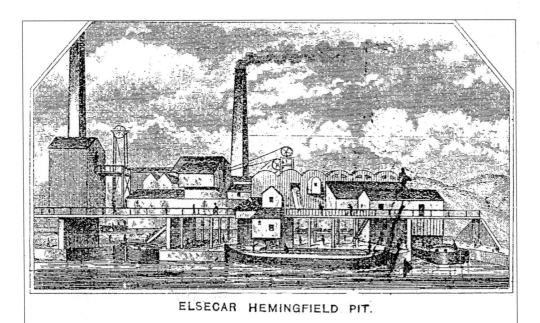

ELSECAR HEMINGFIELD PIT.

Earl Fitzwilliam's Hemingfield Colliery, part of the Elsecar complex, in the 1880s.

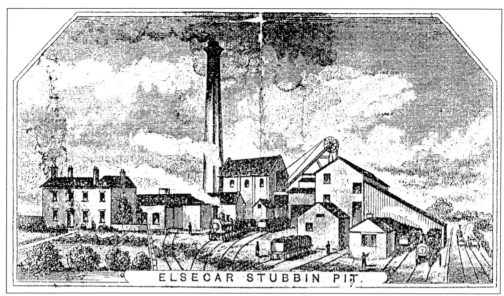

Fitzwilliam's (Old) Stubbin Colliery in the 1880s

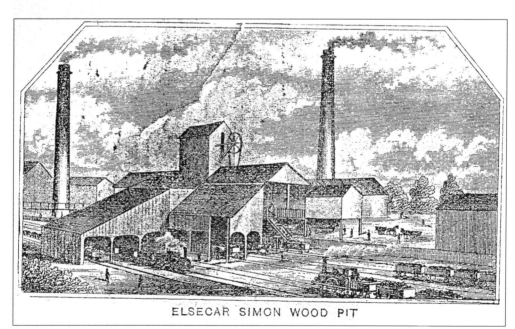

Fitwilliam's Simon Wood Pit at Elsecar in the 1880s.

EARL FITZWILLIAM'S ELSECAR COLLIERY, NEAR ROTHERHAM.

March 29th 184 6

DELIVERED to Captain _____

on account of _Messrs Newton Chambers_

Tons.	Cwts.	qrs.		Per Ton.	£	s.	d.
			Hard Coal, - - - - -				
			Soft Coal, - - - - -				
36			Slack, - - - - -				
			Foundry Coke, —————————	15/			
			Soft Coal Coke, - - - -				
			Railway Coke, - - - -				
			Screened Slack, - - - -				

Joshua Cooper

To Mr Fredk True Downham

An Elsecar Colliery billhead used in 1846. Steamship transport was actually only available from Goole and railway transport only came to Elsecar in 1850. The varieties of coal, coke and slack are identified.

Elsecar underground. Old workings passed through by the Elsecar Footrill (walkway into the pit bottom), *c.*1970.

Testing for gas before entering. The Elsecar Footrill's entrance in Elsecar, *c*.1970.

The Elsecar Footril, passing the blocked-off entrances to old workings.

Wentworth coal, from Earl Fitzwilliam's estate, quoted on the London Coal Exchange in 1802.

To my Workmen at Low Stubbin and Elsecar.

I am informed that you have applied to Mr. NEWBOULD to be re-engaged as my workmen, but before I can give any reply to that request I wish to lay some considerations before you.

I have always refused to belong to any association or federation which might fetter me in my dealings with my workmen ; and I wish to secure for them the same absolute freedom to be or not to be members of any association or federation as they think best.

There have been no difficulties or differences between us respecting wages ; I believe you had no cause for complaint ; so that I am at a loss to know why you laid my pits idle.

So late as the 25th of July last I had the pleasure of seeing you all at my house and receiving a most gratifying proof of your kindly feeling and good will towards me and mine ; and among my most valued possessions is a beautiful book which you gave me. In it are inscribed the names and length of service of all who were in my employment. There I see that many had worked 20, some 30, and some even 50 years and more for me and for my father before me.

Such ties as these create strong regard on both sides and are not easily broken.

I am therefore driven to believe that it was intimidation only which caused you to leave your work ; and those who led you to do so are responsible for the whole of the suffering which you and your families have endured for so long, and also for the want and misery of so many others who have been thrown out of work by your action.

There will always be differences of opinion among men, but if we can bear in mind the Divine command " to do unto others as we would they should do unto us " those differences will never assume any formidable dimensions.

There cannot be a more false or dangerous doctrine than the belief that the interests of employer and employed are opposed to each other. Their real interests must always be one and the same, and they must stand or fall together.

If my pits are re-opened it must be on the understanding that there is an entire absence of intimidation among my workmen, and that they will not interfere with each other whether they are or are not members of any federation.

I am too far off to have an interview with you myself, but if you can satisfy my representatives that there shall be absolute freedom for you all, I shall gladly welcome back to my employment as many as possible.

Yours faithfully,

(Signed), FITZWILLIAM.

COOLLATTIN,
24th Nov., 1893.

Earl Fitzwilliam sends an autocratically worded circular letter to his workmen after the great strike of 1893.

Elsecar pit bottom, *c*.1943.

Telephone :—39 Hoyland.   Telegraphic Address :—" Durnford, Elsecar."

THESE collieries, situated in the heart of the great Yorkshire Coalfield, midway between Barnsley and Rotherham, are the oldest in the county, having been worked continuously by Lord Fitzwilliam and his predecessors for nearly two hundred years. As new pits have been sunk from time to time with a view to maintain and increase the output, they have always been equipped with the most up-to-date and modern apparatus and machin-

ELSECAR MAIN PIT.

A view of the new Elsecar Main Colliery, *c*.1913.

Elsecar village in its rural setting.

PROGRAMME
—AND—
TIME TABLE
OF THE
MOTOR TRIP

OF THE
Elsecar Collieries Officials and Staff, and
the Tradesmen of Elsecar and Hoyland,
—TO—
Dovedale, Matlock, &c.

Tuesday, July 29th, 1919.

A trip for the Elsecar Collieries'
officials and staff and the
tradesmen of the area in 1919.

R.165-501.   Wentworth Woodhouse.   Copyright.   Scrivens.

Profits from the collieries and other mineral rents went in part to support this enormous house (and the Earls Fitzwilliam had others too!).

592 EARL FITZWILLIAM'S FOX HOUNDS.

Another view of Wentworth Woodhouse – with the longest facade in England – and of the Earl's foxhounds. A postcard used in 1905.

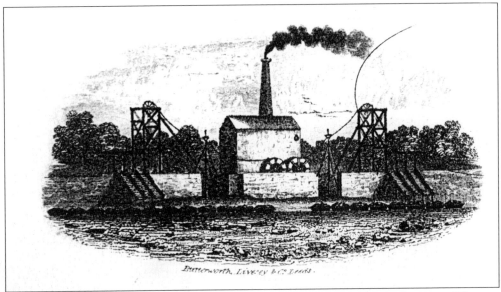

The successive Earls Fitzwilliam worked part of their own coal and leased other parts. This is a view of the tenant Hoyland & Elsecar Coal Co.'s colliery, used on a billhead of 1848.

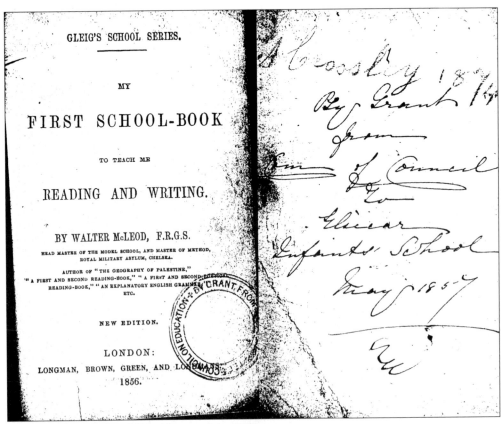

Elsecar Colliery Infants' School at work in 1857.

Elsecar canal basin (the canal was opened here in 1798) with a boat loaded with pit props and another awaiting loading from the coal staith to the right. Note the large colliery ventilating fan housing in the background. Undated.

Colliers' housing at Elsecar. Old Row, probably constructed in the 1790s, in 1963.

Jane Shawcroft — Husband's Name. John — Coal Miner
— 31

Hoyland —
Elizh — *&nens*
Mary — 3

resided in Hoyland rather more than 4 years — Husband died rather more than 12 Months since

Came from Stanley to Hoyland. resided 2 years in Stanley. — House in Stanley

Came from Hoyland to Stanley — resided in Hoyland better than 5 years in lodgings as a single Man

Came from Summer Coats in Derbyshire to Hoyland born in Summer Coats. Where his father 7 years resided before him in Summercoats — & are settled received Relief from then.

7 years since married to Hoyland.

_____

Harley said — Puddler at resided in Hoyland rather more than 18 years

Mary Ann 55
Hoyland House Keeper

= Went to Sheffield Infirmary on 3 weeks there

in a few weeks after applied for Relief 2/6 per Week

A collier's biography: he died in 1849, having originally come from Derbyshire to Elsecar, moved to Stanley near Wakefield and then returned. The document is concerned with the responsibility for poor law relief for his widow in 1850.

The colliers' Union is well supported at Elsecar Colliery in its first year, 1858.

MINERS' ASSOCIATION.
BARNSLEY DISTRICT.

IN order to show the Public that the money received by the Miners' Association is expended for legitimate objects, the following is the expenditure for the fortnight ending Dec. 6th, 1858 :—

	£	s.	d.	£	s.	d.
Money received from the collieries in the district and the public, with the balance in hand				749	7	10½
EXPENDITURE.						
Swinton Lodge	94	13	5			
Rawmarsh Lodge	149	9	7			
Kilnhurst Lodge	30	19	3			
New Parkgate, No. 1, do.	80	6	3			
New Parkgate, No. 2, do.	114	9	0			
Elsecar do.	257	17	4			
District expenses	10	6	0½			
				738	0	10½
Balance in hand				11	7	0
				£749	7	10½

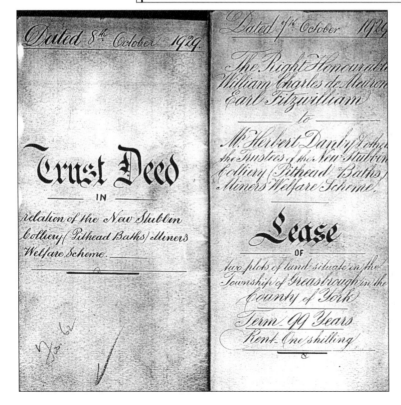

Early colliery baths are provided at New Stubbin Colliery in 1929.

A three-dimensional plaque showing a collier at work ripping coal.

A watercolour painting of a collier at work ripping coal.

Edmunds Main Colliery in the Worsborough valley in 1859, in the valley of the river Dove and loading coal onto the Worsborough branch of the Dearne & Dove Canal in 1859.

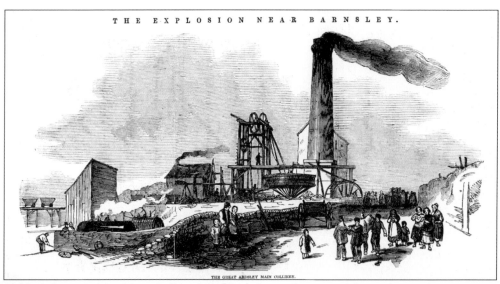

THE EXPLOSION NEAR BARNSLEY.

THE GREAT ARDSLEY MAIN COLLIERY.

(Old) Oaks or Ardsley Main Colliery, near Barnsley at the time of the explosion there in 1847.

MOUNT-OSBORNE COLLIERIES.

Mr. E. Bromley   Barnsley. 29 Sept 18 71

COALS.			SLACK.			Price.	Leading.	£	s.	d.
Tons.	Cwts.	Qrs.	Tons.	Cwts.	Qrs.					
1	10					5/			5	6

TERMS:—Cash on Delivery.
£   s.   d.

From WILLIAM DAY.

Mount Osborne Collieries – with a number of pits near Barnsley: a coal bill of 1871, shewing coal sold at the pit at 5s a ton.

The Darley Main explosion of 1849. Darley Main Colliery (initially known as Lob Wood) was served by the Worsbrough branch of the Dearne & Dove Canal, itself opened in 1804. Barnsley Bed coal lying at 131 yards was leased in 1835 by a group of Barnsley tradesmen, and sinking begun. In 1849 the colliery suffered the worst disaster so far in the South Yorkshire coalfield, when of 100 men and boys in the pit, seventy-five were killed. A relief fund had to be established for the benefit of their dependants.

Transport was improved when the South Yorkshire Railway's branch into the valley was opened as far as Darley Main in mid-1850 and approached over the canal by an oblique, low-level lifting railway bridge. In 1855 the then partners decided to try the nearby Wombwell coalfield, but gave it up as too difficult to work. The Barnsley seam produced 9,000 tons per acre and the nearby Pindar Oaks Colliery was sunk subsequently under a lease of 1866, but the whole colliery closed, exhausted, in 1885.

DREADFUL EXPLOSION
AT THE
DARLEY - MAIN COLLIERY,
NEAR BARNSLEY.

75 LIVES LOST.

ON WEDNESDAY, JANUARY 24th, 1849, about 11 o'clock, a most dreadful EXPLOSION took place at Mr. G. JARRATT JARRATT's COLLIERY, called the DARLEY MAIN COLLIERY, at which time 100 persons were working in the Pit. The sacrifice of life which followed is the greatest which has taken place in any Colliery Explosion in this County, (exceeding even the dreadful catastrophe at the Oaks Colliery in March 1847.)

The Explosion so perceptibly felt on the surface of the ground, in the locality of the place, soon caused hundreds of persons to hurry to the scene, amongst the foremost of which, were to be seen the almost frantic wives, parents, and friends of the unfortunate Miners, for whose safety the worst apprehensions were felt.

The most effectual assistance was immediately rendered by the prompt help of those on the top of the shaft, and as quickly as possible the descent was made into the Pit, where the most awful condition was presented by the sufferers that can possibly be imagined,— a considerable number of the maimed and burnt, and what few were miraculously preserved unhurt, were in and near to the bottom of the shaft, fearfully and anxiously waiting for a deliverance from their dreadful position, and who were very promptly extricated.

It was unhappily too soon ascertained that the greater part of the Miners and others employed in the Pit were buried in the devastation caused by the Explosion ; and up to THURSDAY NIGHT the 25th INST., not less than 75 dead bodies were lying in the adjoining houses and buildings contiguous to the place, the greater part of whom were found dead in the workings at the bottom of the Pit.

The following are the Names of those whose lives have been sacrificed in this appalling calamity :—

MARRIED MEN.	SINGLE MEN & BOYS.
Henry Firth, aged 34, Wife and 4 Children.	Edward Rennison, aged 18.
Joseph Sagar, aged 29, Wife and 6 Children.	Abraham Sykes, aged 25.
	John Sykes, aged 18.
John Burton, aged 26, Wife.	Robert Winter, aged 28.
George Beffit, aged 26, Wife and 1 Child.	George Fisher, aged 23.
	James Ashton, *alias* Lancashire Jim, aged 17.
William Humbleby, aged 35, Wife and 4 Children.	William Guest, aged 15.
	Charles Wood, aged 17.
Edward Utley, aged 36, Wife.	James Birkinshaw, aged 19
John Winder, aged 31, Wife and 4 Children.	Hugh Birkinshaw, aged 22,
	Edward Billington, aged 24.
Francis Wilson, aged 69, Wife.	William Billington, aged 11.
Amos Harper, aged 37, Wife and 7 Children.	Thomas Humbleby, aged 12.
	Thomas Littlewood, aged 11.
Charles Brook, aged 37, 3 Children.	Francis Batty, aged 15.
George Guest, aged 41, Wife and 1 Child.	William Hutchinson, aged 24.
	John Charlesworth, aged 13.
George Loy, aged 40, Wife and 5	Joseph Charlesworth, aged 14

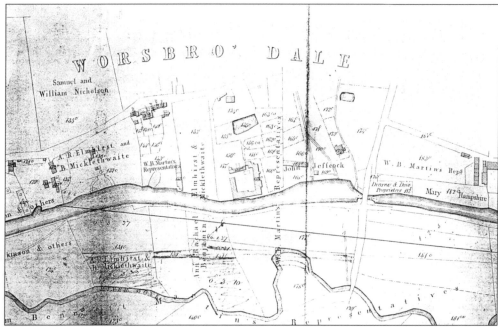

Darley Main Colliery staith (to the west of the bridge) in the mid 1840s, with the line of the proposed railway to the south. A moving bridge had to be constructed over the canal to connect with the new railway opened in 1850.

THE
Late EXPLOSION
AND
LOSS of LIFE
AT
DARLEY-MAIN COLLIERY,
Near BARNSLEY.

BY the above melancholy Accident, **31 married Men** and **44 unmarried Men and Boys** have lost their Lives. **31 Widows** and **55 Children** have been left in a state of great Distress. As soon as possible after the event a Committee was formed, of which **FREDERICK W. T. VERNON WENTWORTH**, Esq., of Wentworth-Castle, will kindly act as the Chairman; **SAMUEL SHARP**, Esq., of Darley-Hall, near Barnsley, was appointed the Secretary; and "The Wakefield and Barnsley Union Banking Company, in Barnsley," were appointed the Treasurers. The objects of the Committee will be to raise a Fund for the Relief of the surviving Sufferers, and the Widows, Orphans, and Families of those who are dead, in addition to, but independently of, such Relief as the Parochial Authorities and the Magistrates of the District may direct to be given. The Education and Apprenticeship of the Orphan Children will be one object of the attention of the Committee.

The Darley-Main Company have commenced the Subscription with a Donation of **£200**, besides having defrayed all the Expenses of the Funerals; and John Jeffcock, Esq., the Owner of the Coal Field, has contributed **£100**.

It is earnestly requested that charitably-disposed Persons in every Parish or Township will kindly raise Subscriptions amongst their Friends and Neighbours, and that all Bankers will solicit Contributions from their respective connexions.

All Sums so to be collected, must be transmitted either to the Secretary or to the Treasurers at their respective Addresses before mentioned.

SAMUEL SHARP,

A public appeal by the owners of the Darley Main colliery after the explosion of 1849.

Coked coal, together with the local availability of both ironstone and fluxing limestone, allowed the development of a large South Yorkshire iron industry. This view of the Thorncliffe Ironworks shows the works in 1825, with loaded wagons in the background.

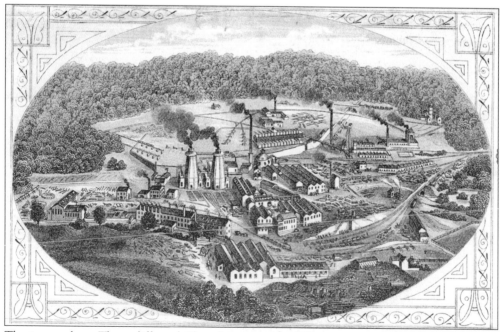

The ironworks at Thorncliffe and Chapeltown in the 1880s.

The great Yorkshire firm of J.&J. Charlesworth was founded in the 1770s in West Yorkshire and developed rapidly and successfully from the 1820s when the firm opened collieries in the Silkstone valley, close to the Barnsley Canal. More collieries followed early in the 1830s at Billingley to the east of Barnsley, but were given up by the 1850s, and at Swinton and Rawmarsh, close to the Don Navigation and the incipient Sheffield & Rotherham Railway. The Milkstone, and later adjoining Dodworth, collieries were developed into a large concern and sold off in the coal boom of the early 1870s to the newly-formed Old Hilkstone & Dodworth Coal & Iron Co. Ltd.

However, the Warren Vale, Kilnhurst and Thrybergh Hall collieries – valued in 1889 at a very substantial £166,366 12s 6d – were successful and were retained. In 1892 they were described as 'one of the largest vendors of coal in England', working under 1,500 acres of South Yorkshire. In 1927 their Don valley pits were finally sold off to Stewarts & Lloyds, the steel manufacturers of Birmingham. The Kilnhurst Colliery was worked until 1986.

They were good employers providing high standard cottages, schools and sporting facilities for their workforce and their families, and supported trades union organisation among their men. They got a handsome write-up in the Miners' National Association meetings held in 1863.

MESSRS. J. & J. CHARLESWORTH'S COLLIERIES.

PRICE PER TON AT THE STAITHS.

HAIGH MOOR, AT STANLEY FERRY,

AND AT BOTTOM BOAT, BELOW WAKEFIELD.

	CREDIT. s. d.	MONEY. s. d.
Coals	6 2	6 0
Coal Cinders	13 0	
Riddled Slack	3 9	

VICTORIA,

AT BOTTOM BOAT.

	s. d.	s. d.
Coals	6 6	6 3
Coal Cinders	13 0	
Riddled Slack	3 9	

NEW MARKET,

AT BOTTOM BOAT.

	s. d.	s. d.
Lofthouse	6 0	5 9
Warren House	4 6	
Riddled Slack	3 9	

ROBIN HOOD,

AT BOTTOM BOAT.

	s. d.	s. d.
Low Main	6 2	6 0
High Main, Good House Coal ...	6 3	6 1
Steam and Lime Coal	5 0	
—— Ditto ——	4 0	
Riddled Slack	3 9	
Slack Cinders	7 0	

HAIGH MOOR,

(LATE FENTON'S) AT BOTTOM BOAT.

	s. d.	s. d.
Coals	6 2	6 0
Riddled Slack	3 9	
Cinders	6 0	

A price list from 1848 of coals from J.&J. Charlesworths' West and South Yorkshire collieries.

LOFTHOUSE,

(LATE FENTON'S) AT BOTTOM BOAT.

	CREDIT. s. d.	MONEY. s. d.
Coals	6 0	5 9
Riddled Slack	3 9	

River Dues on Coals shipped at Bottom Boat, to the Tideway at Goole, 1s. 3d. per Ton; to the Tideway at Selby, 1s. 0½d. per Ton.

ROTHWELL HAIGH,

LEEDS RIVER.

	s. d.	s. d.
Best Coal	6 0	5 9
Seconds Coal	4 7	4 4
Top Coal	5 2	5 0
Slack Cinders	7 0	
Riddled Slack	3 9	
Screen Slack	2 0	

River Dues on Rothwell Haigh Coals to the Tideway at Goole, 1s. 1½d. per Ton.

SILKSTONE,

BARNSLEY CANAL.

	s. d.	s. d.
Silkstone Coal	6 0	5 9
Riddled Slack	3 6	
Slack Cinders, per Ton	5 0	

Canal and River Dues on Silkstone Coal to the Tideway at Goole, 2s. 7½d. per Ton.

FLOCKTON,

AT HORBURY BRIDGE.

	s. d.	s. d.
Flockton Coal	7 3	7 0
Common Ditto		
Riddled Slack	3 6	

Canal and River Dues on Flockton Coal to the Tideway at Goole, 2s. 0½d. per Ton.

HOLLING HALL,

WAKEFIELD.

	s. d.	s. d.
Winter Coal	5 6	5 3
Bimshaw Coal	4 6	
Coal Cinders	12 0	

River Dues on Holling Hall Coals to the Tideway at Goole, 1s. 7½d. per Ton.

NETHERTON,

THREE MILES ABOVE WAKEFIELD.

	CREDIT. s. d.	MONEY. s. d.
Best Coal	4 9	4 6
Lime and Common Coal	4 0	3 9
Engine Coal	3 0	

River Dues on the Netherton Coals to the Tideway at Goole, 1s. 10½d. per Ton.

KILNHURST,

RIVER DUNN, NEAR ROTHERHAM.

	s. d.	s. d.
Nine Feet Coal (for Steam Packets)	6 3	6 0
——Ditto——Hards and Softs ...	5 9	5 6
——Ditto——Softs	5 0	4 9
Kent's Main	5 0	4 9
Coal Cinders, per Dozen	9 6	9 0
——Ditto——per Ton	13 0	12 6
Riddled Slack	3 0	
Unriddled Slack	1 6	

River Dues on Kilnhurst Coals to the Tideway at Goole, 10d. per Ton.
Do. Do. Slack Do. Do. 5d. ,,

Lofthouse, Wakefield, 1848.

41

Valuation of the different Coll[?]

Feby 15th 1847

Roth well Hough	17135 - 17 - 6
Robin Hood	12618 - 14 - 11
Ardsley	2554 - 11 - 0
New Market	5493 - 2 - 2
Bottom Boat	2312 - 5 - 9
Bushey Cliff	310 - 0 - 0
Oak Wood	7600 - 14 - 9
Outcorn	1030 - 15 - 0
Hartly Bank	796 - 7 - 4
Flockton	3464 - 2 - 0
Old Silkston	4936 - 7 - 1
New do	10820 - 0 - 1
Roomack	6385 - 19 - 9
Longley Shops	108 - 2 - 7
Lofthous do	123 - 3 - 2
do Warehouse	782 - 8 - 0
Leeds Staiths	501 - 14 - 0
Huddersfield	70 - 0 - 0

```
               7362.12.7    78244 - 5 - 7
                  56  7 - 0      218 - 7 - 0
Douworth ——— 77418-19-7  78462  12 - 7
                          77362  12 - 7
```

Valuation of Charlesworths' various collieries in 1847.

Valuation of Charlesworths' collieries in 1889.

Kilnhurst Colliery	[illegible]		82800	10	8
Thrybergh Hall	Do	Do	78066	1	10
Rothwell Haigh	Do	Do	94325	5	8
Robin Hood	Do	Do	47749	3	0
Newmarket	Do	Do	87359	4	11
Haigh Moor	Do	Do	24310	0	0
Briquette Works	Do	Do	2330	4	9
Land Cottages &c	Stanley near Briquette Works		500	0	0
Staithes Buildings &c	Land at Kilnhurst [illegible]		5000	0	0
Goodwill			24579	9	2
		Total £	400000	0	0

2330	4	9
500		
£2830	4	9
5500		
8330	4	9

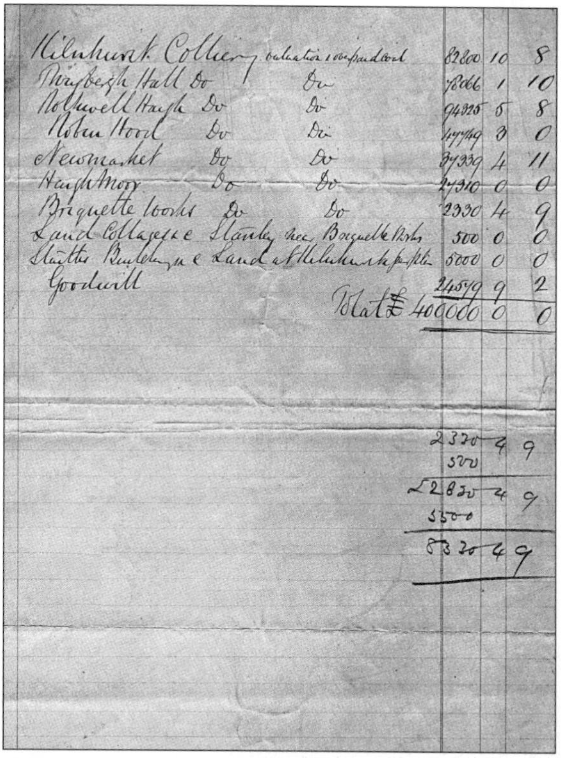

Charlesworths' railway waggon consignment note, coal from their Old Silkstone Collieries in 1853.

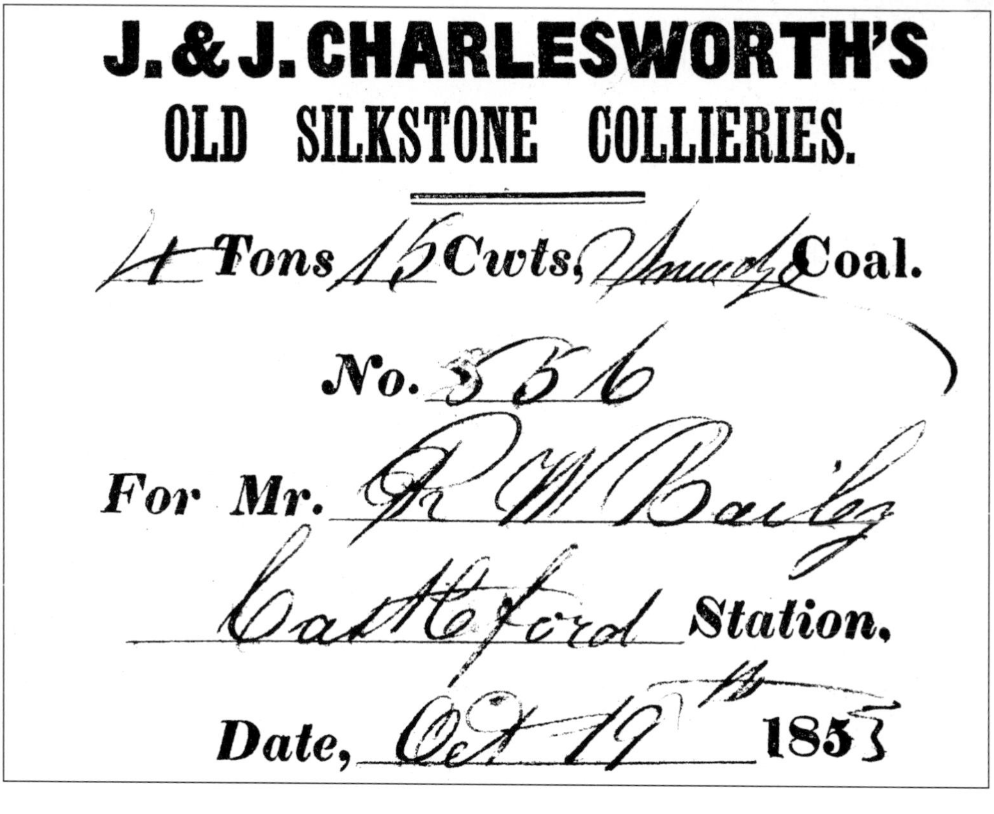

J. & J. CHARLESWORTH'S

OLD SILKSTONE COLLIERIES.

4 Tons 15 Cwts, [illegible] Coal.

No. 556

For Mr. R W Bailey

Castleford Station.

Date, Oct 19th 1853

The working gear of Charlesworths' colliery pumping engine at Kilnhurst Colliery.

The cylinder top of Kilnhurst Colliery's beam pumping engine.

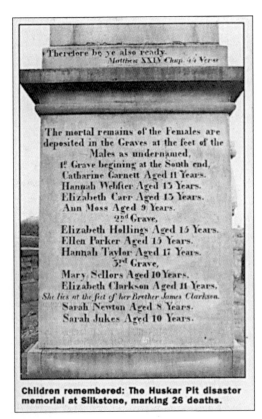

Clarke's Silkstone Collieries: the monument in Silkstone churchyard to mark the burial of the girls who were killed by a flash flood in 1838 at the Husker Pit. In all, twenty-six children were drowned.

. SHAFTON COLLIERY,

Mr Josh Jackson Smeaton

TO PROCTORS & WATSON.

[ACCOUNTS TO BE PAID HALF-YEARLY]

		Tons.	Cwts.	Price.	£.	s.	d.
1847 Sept. 22	*To 9 C. Coals*					*9*	
" 29	*To 9 do do*					*9*	
						18	
1848 Jany 13th	*Settled*						
	Wm Procter						

Shafton Colliery, working in an area where a plan of 1597 shows coal workings, was one of many which never possessed either waterway or railway connections. It still supplied local rural areas and this continued well into the nineteenth century, even possessing (as shown here) a market selling to a farmer at Kirk Smeaton in 1847; over eight miles away as the crow flies. The colliery was apparently closed between 1861 and 1864.

A boat on the Barnsley Canal, apparently loaded with large pieces of coal.

A canal roving bridge on the Barnsley Canal – one where the towpath changed sides.

The lock controlling the flow of water between rival waterways' routes at Barnsley at the junction of the Barnsley and Dearne & Dove Canals.

A Don-sized Yorkshire sailing keel passing through the narrow cut at Sprotborough from a postcard used in 1911.

The narrowboat Chesterfield passed through the southern-most tip of South Yorkshire and served local collieries. This is the western portal of the 2,850 yards long Norwood Tunnel.

The canal was opened in 1777 and the section through South Yorkshire closed in c.1908

A typical lock on the Chesterfield Canal between South Yorkshire and the tideway in the Trent.

The Silkstone Railway of the Barnsley Canal Co., carrying coal from close to the pitheads down to the terminal basin at Barnby Bridge near Cawthorne, was opened in 1809 and its rails lifted in the early 1870s. Here are stone sleeper blocks near Silkstone village. The railway was continued by private branches.

CORPORATION WHARF   WATH-ON-DEARNE   W. E. FARTHING

The Dearne & Dove Canal, connecting Barnsley with the Don navigation at Swinton, was opened 1804. Here a sailing keel is at Wath-on-Dearne. From a postcard used in 1907.

Seagoing vessels on the Trent awaiting loading with coal at Keadby, the outfall of the Stainforth & Keadby Canal which connected the Don valley pits with the tideway and was opened in about 1802.

Sailing keels and small steamers at Thorne on the Stainforth & Keadby Canal at Keadby.

The aqueduct over the river Dearne below the town of Barnsley which carried the coal-based Barnsley canal to the navigable river Calder at Wakefield. It was opened in 1799.

Sinking a boring shaft the old way; probably in South Yorkshire and certainly photographed by a Barnsley amateur.

Above and overleaf: The Oaks Colliery – later known as Old Oaks – was projected from its beginnings in 1835 as a large undertaking and initially developed by the Ardsley Mining Co. It was sold to the firm of Barber, Walker & Co. in 1845, and coal from it was exhibited at the Great Exhibition of 1851. In the 1850s it possessed large markets in London and shipped its steam-raising Barnsley Bed coal from the ports of Liverpool, Garston, Birkenhead, Hull and Grimsby. It suffered a disaster in 1866 that caused 364 deaths, by far the largest death toll in the whole Yorkshire coalfield, and work began in 1868 on the sinking of a New Oaks Colliery, and in 1892 on new sinkings at Old Oaks too.

GENERAL VIEW OF THE OAKS COLLIERY, BARNSLEY, THE SCENE OF THE LATE DISASTER.—SEE PAGE 66.

TO COLLIERY PROPRIETORS, CON-
TRACTORS, SINKERS, AND OTHERS.
Sale of Capital Twelve-Horse High-pressure Engine
and Boilers; excellent Wind Bore Pumping Gear;
L Leg; Blowing Georges, Air-Pipes, Gin, Wire
and Hemp Ropes, Pullies, Sinkers' Trunks, Centres,
Crabbes, Drills, Picks, Wedges, Hammers, and other
Tools and Materials; with Two useful Horses,
broad-wheeled Carts, Straw-Chopper, &c.

MR. LANCASTER has received instructions
from Messrs. W. TAYLOR, Jun., and Co., to
SELL BY AUCTION,
AT THE LOW ELSECAR (LATE LUND HILL) COLLIERY,
ON THURSDAY, the 27th of DECEMBER, 1855,
In consequence of the Completion of their Sinkings:
ALL THE SURPLUS
SINKING IMPLEMENTS
And MATERIALS, which are in excellent condition,
Comprising—
A capital 12-Horse High-Pressure
HORIZONTAL WINDING ENGINE,
With Patent Piston, by *Elliss*, of Manchester; together
with Winding Drum, Spur Gearing, and Pedestals
complete.
HIGH-PRESSURE BOILER,
24 feet long, by 4 feet diameter; with the Mountings,
Grate-Bars, and Doors complete.
A VERY CAPITAL HIGH-PRESSURE BOILER,
21 feet long by 5 feet 6 in. diameter, with Mountings,
Grate-Bars, and Doors in excellent condition. Second-
hand 10-horse Low-Pressure Hay-cock BOILER.

1 excellent WINDING DRUM, 5 feet diameter,
6 feet long, cast metal ends, metal centre, with
wall plates, pedestals, foundation bolts, and ashlar
foundation, with pair of Driving Wheels, 4 feet and
17 inches diameter.

Slide WIND BORE, turned through, 11 feet 6 inches
long, 12 inches diameter.

160 yards of Air Pipes, 16 inches by 12 inches, in
good condition.

Powerful GIN, with Head Stocks and platform; 1
Double-purchase CRAB; 1 single ditto.

2 New Metal Cribs, adapted for a ten-foot pit.

2 Excellent Iron BLOW GEORGES, nearly new,
3 feet 6 inches diameter.

3 Pairs of 5 ft., 4 ft., and 2 ft. 6 in. Iron Pulleys,
with Pedestals (for round rope); Pair of excellent
Sinking Head Stocks and Iron Pulley, with Lurry,
&c., equal to new; excellent WIRE ROPE, 300
yards long, 3¼ inches circumference, by Newall and
Co.; Quantity of Second-Hand Hemp Rope; Metal L
Leg and Pedestals, with Spear and pumping motion;
excellent Spur Wheel, 5 feet diameter; Metal Quad-
rant, with Pulley and Hand Wheel; 3 Jack Rolls,
nearly new; 9 Iron Sinking Trunks; 2 Circular
Walling Scaffolds, 11 ft. and 8 ft. diameter; 35
Sinking Drills, 3 Cast Steel Do.; 25 Sinking Picks; 2
Clipeses; Iron Sinking Bull, 2 large Hammers, 15
Stone Wedges, 4 Quarry Picks, 9 Centres, new Cap-
stan, 2 Head Stock Lurries, Iron centre line Pulley,
Quantity Boiler Plating, Metal Piping, Chain, new
Grate Bars, Metal Bearers, Block, &c., 2 Sheet Iron
Oil Cisterns, with Brass Pumps attached; 3 Brick
Tables, Moulds, and Wheelbarrows; Grindstone, 3
feet diameter; 4 Metal Wall Plates, Bellows, and
other valuable Materials. Also,
A USEFUL BROWN HORSE, 7 years old; BROWN
MARE, 8 years old;
2 broad-wheeled Carts, with Sideboards; Straw-
Chopper; &c., &c.

Sale to commence precisely at Twelve o'clock.

The arrival and departure trains at Wombwell station,
which is distant half-a-mile from the Colliery, are at
convenient hours for parties attending the sale.

Selling off the shaft sinking
equipment used at Lund Hill Colliery,
1855.

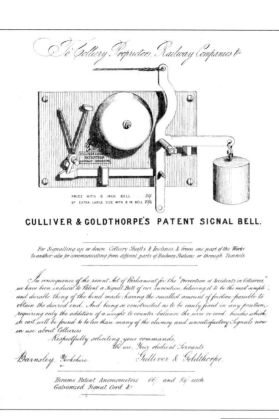

CULLIVER & GOLDTHORPE'S PATENT SIGNAL BELL.

For Signalling up or down Colliery Shafts & Inclines & from one part of the Works to another; also for communicating from different parts of Railway Stations or through Tunnels

In consequence of the recent Act of Parliament for the "Prevention of Accidents in Collieries," we have been induced to Patent a Signal Bell of our Invention, believing it to be the most simple and durable thing of the kind made; having the smallest amount of friction possible to obtain the desired end. And being so constructed as to be easily fixed in any position, requiring only the addition of a weight to counter-balance the wire or cord: besides which, its cost will be found to be less than many of the clumsy and unsatisfactory Signals now in use about Collieries.

Respectfully soliciting your commands,

We are, Your obedient Servants

Barnsley, Yorkshire.   *Gulliver & Goldthorpe.*

Biram's Patent Anemometers 66/ and 84/ each
Galvanized Signal Cord &c

Advertisement of a patent signal bell used in collieries, with a range of testimonials from South Yorkshire colliery owners, c.1860. Its makers described themselves as iron and steel merchants, wholesale and retail ironmongers, locksmiths, whitesmiths and bell hangers on Market Hill, Barnsley in the trade directories of 1857 to 1862.

TESTIMONIALS.

HOYLAND AND ELSECAR COLLIERY, BARNSLEY.

GENTLEMEN,
In reply to your letter respecting your Signal Bell for Colliery purposes, I have much pleasure in testifying as to its simplicity and efficiency, having had it in full operation ever since its arrival.
I am, Gentlemen,
Yours truly,
CHARLES WEBSTER.
Messrs. Gulliver and Goldthorpe.

WOMBWELL MAIN COLLIERY,

GENTLEMEN,
I have much pleasure in testifying as to the unquestionable superiority of your Signal Bell over all others I have hitherto seen, not only in simplicity and evident powers of durability, but in that great desideratum Cheapness.
I will thank you to furnish this Company with two more at your early convenience.
Yours very truly,
WM. P. MADDISON.
Messrs. Gulliver and Goldthorpe,
Barnsley.

MINERAL OFFICE, WENTWORTH WOODHOUSE, ROTHERHAM,

GENTLEMEN,
I like the construction of your Signal Bells for the use of Collieries, which appear to me to be as simple, effective, and economical an arrangement as one could conceive.
In addition to those I ordered of you for Elsecar Colliery, please to send six more—on Earl Fitzwilliam's account—for Park-Gate Colliery.
I am, Gentlemen,
Respectfully yours,
BEN. BIRAM.
Messrs. Gulliver and Goldthorpe,
Barnsley.

OAKS COLLIERY, NEAR BARNSLEY.

GENTLEMEN,
I am very much pleased with your Signal Bell. The simplicity of its mechanism, and certainty of its action, render it the most complete, safe, and durable signal—for either Railway or Colliery purposes—that I have seen. I am quite sure that its great utility, together with its low price, will establish its superiority over the Signals now used in the Collieries both in the North of England and also in the Midland Counties.
I am, Gentlemen,
Yours very truly,
JOSEPH COE.
Messrs. Gulliver and Goldthorpe.

MOUNT OSBORNE COLLIERIES, BARNSLEY.

GENTLEMEN,
Having examined your Signal Bell, I have much pleasure in speaking as to its great simplicity and efficiency. It surpasses anything of the kind I have ever yet seen, and I have no doubt but that it will be found valuable as either a Colliery or a Railway Signal.
I am, Gentlemen,
Yours respectfully,
W. A. POTTER.
Messrs. Gulliver and Goldthorpe,
Barnsley.

EDMUND'S MAIN COLLIERY, NEAR BARNSLEY.

GENTLEMEN,
We received the two Signal Bells from you, and I must say that I am much pleased with their construction,—being at once a simple and convenient arrangement, and more every prospect of being durable.
Send, soon as convenient, two more to these Works, and four to the Bell Ing Colliery,
And oblige, Gentlemen,
Yours respectfully,
JOSEPH MITCHELL.
To Messrs. Gulliver and Goldthorpe.

Two
The Railway Age

The Midland Railway Co.'s Barnsley to Cudworth branch opened over this great viaduct in 1870, crossing two canals and other railway routes.

Lund Hill Colliery, sunk in 1854-1856, was one of the early sinkings to develop the Barnsley Bed coal for the new railway-borne markets opening up from 1850. Although initially financially unsuccessful, it was taken over in 1857, the time of the great explosion which killed 189 men and boys, which incident was graphically illustrated in the following engravings, by a group of partners headed by William Stewart, a Wakefield lawyer. The colliery was a financial success under Stewart's management and only closed in 1894 due to the exhaustion of the Barnsley seam workable under its leases. Its shafts were sold to the Wombwell Main Co. nearby. It possessed both railway and canal connections and had the usual long row of colliers' cottages, chapel and school.

THE EXPLOSION AT LUND HILL COLLIERY, BARNSLEY.

Illustrations of the Lund Hill Colliery explosion of 1857.

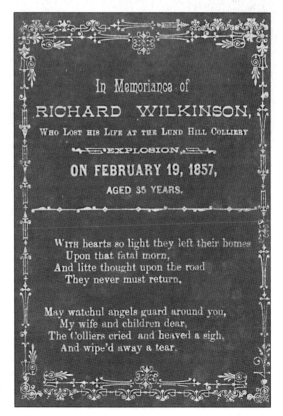

In Memoriance of

RICHARD WILKINSON,

WHO LOST HIS LIFE AT THE LUND HILL COLLIERY

EXPLOSION,

ON FEBRUARY 19, 1857,

AGED 35 YEARS.

WITH hearts so light they left their homes
Upon that fatal morn,
And litte thought upon the road
They never must return.

May watchul angels guard around you,
My wife and children dear,
The Colliers cried and heaved a sigh,
And wipe'd away a tear.

A memorial card to a colliery worker who
died in the Lund Hill explosion of 1857.

Edmunds & Swaithe Collieries were owned by the one company and were notorious as each had been the scene of a major disaster. Beginning in a small way as Bell Ing Colliery in 1845, it closed in 1851 and was taken over by Joseph Mitchell in 1852. Mitchell was an ironfounder and boiler manufacturer, who, in 1854, joined with Tyas and Charles Bartholomew in a new Edmunds Main Coal Company, which sank Edmunds Main (probably opened in 1855) and then Swaithe Main in 1860. Both collieries were closed in 1896, and their coke ovens in c.1908. Edmunds and Swaithe are among the best documented of South Yorkshire collieries.

BARNSLEY INDEPENDENT

Presentation Portrait
Nº 2
ALDERMAN JOHN TYAS ESQ.

From a Photograph by
J. WALKER, BARNSLEY.

WILLIAM TEGGIN, Litho. Manchester.

John Tyas (1817-1895) of Barnsley, solicitor, town councillor, mayor, Tory, High Churchman, Freemason and colliery owner. He became a partner in 1854 in what, in 1879, became the Edmunds & Swaithe Collieries Co. Ltd, and was that concern's managing partner. During the period of his partnership he was witness to the collieries' appalling disasters of 1862 and 1875. The collieries closed shortly after his death.

   Tyas was both an able and a liberal-minded man, taking a leading part in movements, and sometimes initiating them, which were for the benefit of his fellow townspeople of Barnsley.

THE SWAITHE MAIN COLLIERY EXPLOSION, NEAR BARNSLEY: THE COLLIERY.

Above: An engraving of 1875, the time of the Swaithe Main Colliery explosion which killed 143 people, showing a list of those who died.
Below and overleaf: images of the disaster and details of the relief fund set up for its victims.

THE SWAITHE MAIN COLLIERY EXPLOSION, NEAR BARNSLEY: FINDING THE DEAD BODIES.

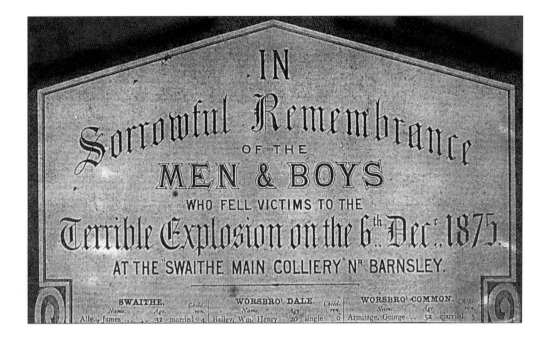

In Sorrowful Remembrance OF THE MEN & BOYS WHO FELL VICTIMS TO THE Terrible Explosion on the 6th Decr. 1875. AT THE "SWAITHE MAIN COLLIERY" Nr BARNSLEY.

SWAITHE.			WORSBRO' DALE.			WORSBRO' COMMON.		
Name.	Age.	Children	Name.	Age.	Children	Name.	Age.	Children
Allen, James	32	married 4	Bailey, Wm. Henry	20	single 0	Armitage, George	52	married 5

SWAITHE MAIN COLLIERY EXPLOSION FUND.

At a Public Meeting of the Inhabitants of Barnsley and its Vicinity, held in the Town Hall, on the 17th December, 1875, for the purpose of considering what arrangements should be made towards providing a Fund for the Relief of the Widows, Orphans, and Sufferers by the Explosion of the Swaithe Main Colliery, RICHARD CARTER, Esq., Mayor of Barnsley, presiding,

It was unanimously resolved,—

"That this Meeting has heard with heartfelt regret of the frightful calamity that occurred at the "Swaithe Main Colliery, on Monday, the 6th of December, when 143 lives were sacrificed "by an explosion of fire-damp, and records its deepest sympathy with the Widows, Orphans, and "Sufferers caused thereby."

A Provisional Committee was appointed for the purpose of receiving Subscriptions towards the immediate and permanent relief of the Sufferers by the Explosion, and for the purpose of obtaining assistance from any Funds heretofore subscribed for the relief of those from former explosions, and for taking steps to form a Permanent Fund to meet casualties of a like nature in the West Riding of Yorkshire.

At an adjourned Public Meeting, held on Friday, the 25th day of February, 1876, for the purpose of receiving the Report of the Provisional Committee, Mr. W. H. Peacock, the Honorary Secretary, read the following report :—

"The Subjects submitted to the Committee were three in number :—

I. To receive Subscriptions for the Relief of the Sufferers.

II. The availability of Existing Funds for the like purpose.

III. The Formation of a Permanent Fund applicable to Colliery Accidents in the West Riding.

"Your Committee have had prominently before them four existing Funds, namely, the Old Oaks Fund, "£700 ; the Hartley Fund (with interest £510 11s. 0d.), £2,795 8s. 4d.; the New Oaks Fund, £29,000 ; "and the Mansion House Fund.

"It would appear that the £700 remaining of the original Oaks Fund could be handed over towards "forming a Permanent Fund ; that the accumulated interest upon the Hartley Fund would be avail- "able for the sufferers in the present calamity ; and that the Trustees of the New Oaks Fund would not, "until five years hence, be in a position to contribute any sum of money for the purposes of relief "of Sufferers by this Explosion ; and even then they consider their fund applicable to the Permanent "Fund only, the Trustees of which would exercise their discretion as to its application.

"It will therefore be necessary to appeal to the public on behalf of the present sufferers. There are "75 Widows and 167 Children and other dependents left unprovided for, and your Committee are of "opinion that a sum of from £15,000 to £20,000 will be required for the purposes of relief.

"Your Committee have not been able to take any steps with regard to the formation of a Permanent Fund, "beyond ascertaining that the original Oaks Fund ; the principal of the Hartley Fund ; and the Oaks "Fund of 1866, as before alluded to, will be available for the purpose.

Signed

"Barnsley, 23rd Feb., 1876.

"RICHD. CARTER, Mayor.
"WM. H. PEACOCK, Hon. Sec."

It was then moved by W. S. STANHOPE, Esq., M.P.; Seconded by the Rev. H. J. DAY, and

Resolved,—

"That the Provisional Committee appointed at the former Meeting, held on the 17th day of December last, "be appointed the committee (with power to add to their number) for the collection and distribution of "the Fund to be subscribed for the relief of the Swaithe Main sufferers, with power to take such steps as "they may think proper for carrying out the instructions of this meeting, and that any surplus of any "moneys collected be handed over to the Permanent Fund."

[OVER]

Denaby Main Colliery worked in an area where coal had been produced by the 1480s, and where a large mid eighteenth century colliery had been worked with a steam engine for water pumping. In 1863 a lease was taken and the new Denaby Colliery sunk to the Barnsley seam at $449\frac{1}{2}$ yards, then the deepest pit in Yorkshire; coal was produced from the end of 1868. The partners were largely already experienced as coalmasters in West Yorkshire at West Riding (Altofts) and Sharlston collieries. Houses, a school, a library, a co-operative society, chapels and churches were all built for the new colliery community, and in the new village a large glass-works was begun in 1863, a pottery in 1870 and, by 1901, an explosives works.

Cadeby Colliery, to the east of Denaby, was begun by the same company in 1889. At both collieries, labour relations were poor, and there were numerous evictions of collier families from the company cottages. The seam at Denaby had a poor quality roof to it, and of the total 8-9ft of the Barnsley Bed, only 6-7ft were taken.

Denaby Main closed in 1968 on merging with Cadeby Main, and the whole complex closed in 1986.

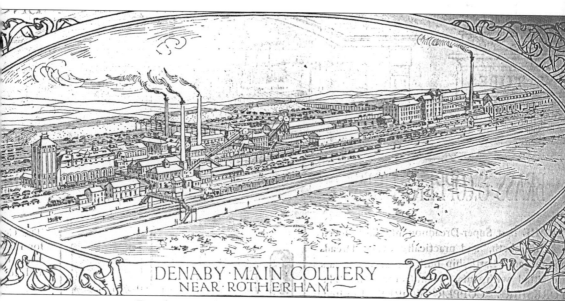

DENABY·MAIN·COLLIERY
NEAR·ROTHERHAM ~

Denaby Main from a drawing published in 1913.

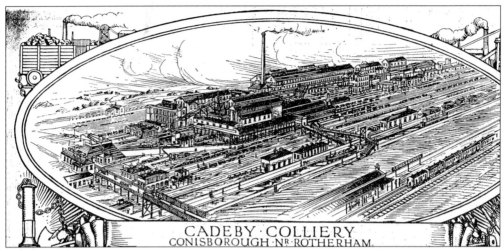

Denaby Main as depicted in 1913.

Denaby Main Colliery Offices – and trolleybus wires.

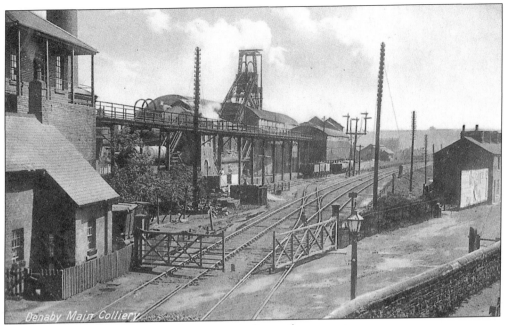

Denaby Main Colliery and the adjoining main line railway crossing.

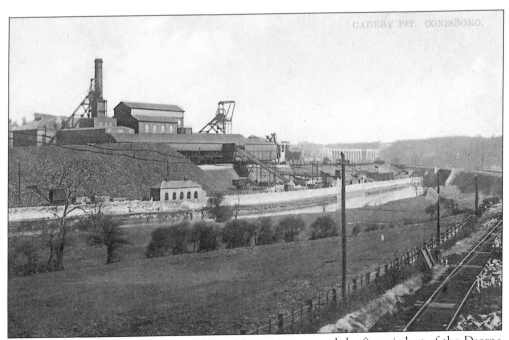

Cadeby Colliery showing the pit, the Don Navigation cut and the fine viaduct of the Dearne Valley Railway, opened to traffic in 1909.

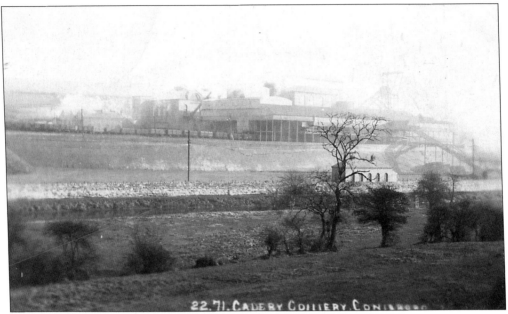

Cadeby Colliery, with many waggons awaiting loading.

Cadeby Colliery's boat loading staith on the Don Navigation.

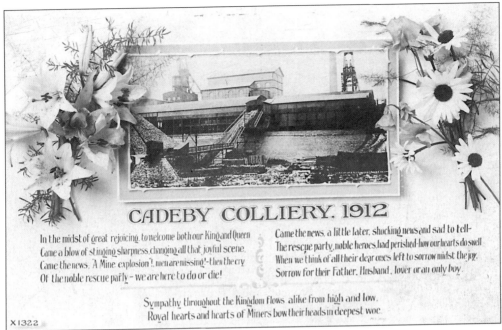

CADEBY COLLIERY. 1912

In the midst of great rejoicing, to welcome both our King and Queen
Came a blow of stinging sharpness, changing all that joyful scene.
Came the news. 'A Mine explosion'! men are missing!'–then the cry
Of the noble rescue party – we are here to do or die!

Came the news, a little later, shocking news and sad to tell–
The rescue party, noble heroes, had perished–how our hearts do swell
When we think of all their dear ones left to sorrow midst the joy.
Sorrow for their Father, Husband, lover or an only boy.

Sympathy throughout the Kingdom flows alike from high and low.
Royal hearts and hearts of Miners bow their heads in deepest woe.

X1322

A postcard commemorating the colliery disaster of 1912.

A pedal-powered rail trolley at Denaby, with the colliery in the background.

A commemorative paper handkerchief for the Cadeby disaster of 1912

Wombwell Main Colliery was sunk under a lease of 1855 in an area recently rejected by the Darley Main Colliery. In fact it was to prove an immensely remunerative concern: the ground was broken for shaft sinking at the end of 1853 and the Barnsley seam won in October 1854 at $224\frac{1}{2}$ yards. The leasing of 1855 presumably reflected the tentative nature of this particular shaft sinking. As it transpired the lease was taken for a period of ninety-nine years.

In 1862 the company was awarded medals for the coal it exhibited at the International Exhibition in London, and in 1868 its coals were used by the English and French navies for steamraising. A Miners' (mutual) Friendly Society was established for Wombwell Main in 1857 and a Wombwell Main Brass Band existed in 1858.

Wombwell Main, which employed 670, closed in 1969.

Wombwell Main Colliery shown on a postcard used in 1915.

Charles Bartholomew, C.E. (d.1895) was engineer to the Don Navigation and, from 1840, its manager. At the same time he was similarly employed by the South Yorkshire Railway and became a member of its Board. With other directors of the railway company he joined in partnership in the sinking of Wombwell Main and Cortonwood collieries, and from 1854 he had been a partner in the Edmunds (and later Edmunds and Swaithe) Colliery.

A man of great ability, he was an author, an inventor and interested in other commercial concerns. He went to live in distant Ealing, but retained his colliery interests and advisory usefulness to the extent of having, in connection with Wombwell Main Colliery at least, a wooden model of the workings at home at Ealing. He added new parts as the workings expanded, while surviving correspondence demonstrates his frequent consultations on the working of Edmunds and Swaithe Mains too.

THE

WOMBWELL MAIN
TEASER

Published by the Wombwell Main Communist group.

THE NEW YEAR CALLS FOR NEW STRUGGLES
STRENGTH TO FIGHT, NOT CHARITY.

What has 1929 to offer for the miners of South Yorkshire in general, or the miners of Wombwell Main in particular? The conditions in the Coalfield get steadily worse. The Eight Hours Act is, in practice, a farce. Unemployment increases on a scale never before known, now reaching 46, 000 in Yorkshire. The hopes in "Industrial Peace" and "Rationalisation" raised by the Labour Leaders have proved the hypocritical deception we foretold they would.

The Five Counties Scheme has been admitted to be a failure by the chairman of the association running it. For the men it has been a stark tragedy. Since January 1927 some 17 pits have been closed down in the S. Yorkshire field.

Improved methods of production have not lead to any extension of employment or of markets. Exports have fallen during the last year. Thus under capitalism THERE IS NO PROSPECT OF BETTER TRADE AND MORE EMPLOYMENT. The only prospect is increasing unemployment and being struck off the Labour Exchange register in April when the new Act comes into operation.

Faced with the ruin of the coal industry under capitalist mismanagement the present Y.M.A. leadership have nothing to offer but co-operation with the coal owners in order that the men can make sacrifices without struggle. They arrogate to themselves de lux expenses , oppose rationalisation of their own organisation and bitterly fight the REDS.

Miners of South Yorkshire you cannot fight individually, you must be organised for struggle in a real fighting Trade Union. The Y.M.A. must be saved from the grip of the old gang and made a real militant union. Only the rank and file can do this. Everywhere SAVE THE UNION COMMITTEES are growing up. They are demanding a ballot on the following issues: - 1. For or against Mondism, 2. For or against the disruption of the Scottish Unions, 3. For or against A.J.Cook as secretary, 4. For or against Herbert Smith as president, 5. For or against the minworkers Union. The rank and file must decide, not unmandated delegates.

Build up SAVE THE UNION committees in every branch. Give in your name to comrades distributing the bulletins. Work and fight to SAVE THE UNION.

Wombwell Main Communist Group's publicity of 1929.

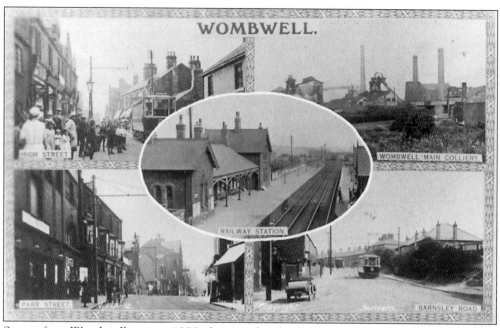

Scenes from Wombwell town, c.1928, showing the electric tramway which operated only from 1924 to 1933.

KILNHURST & THRYBERGH HALL COLLIERIES.

✣ PRICE LIST. ✣

		s.	d.
1.	Tonnage per dozen of 10 tons Unriddled Coal ...	11	8
2.	"End" Headings... ... ... per yard	7	0
3.	"Bord" Headings ... ... "	5	2½
3a.	Wedging in Headings when stopped blowing "End of Bord" ... ... per yard	1	6
4.	Shift Working in "Benks and Posts" per dozen	0	5
5.	Shift Working in Headings ... extra per yard	0	6
6.	Re-opening "Benks or Posts" when fallen in and a rib is left next the goaf ... per yard	4	7
7.	Re-opening "Benks or Posts" when no rib is left "	3	0
8.	Cutting ends in Benks ... ... "	1	10½
9.	Starting a place until 5 yards of face is gained "	3	8
10.	Gatemaking ... ... "	2	2½
11.	Packing (7-ft. 6-in. finish 6-ft. 6-in.) ... "	2	7
12.	Single Wall Packing ... ... "	1	3½
13.	Square Packs to be paid ½ yard extra.		
14.	Setting Bars 6-ft. long in Gates and Faces per bar	0	7
	Do. 7-ft. do. do. "	0	9
	Do. 8-ft. do. do. "	0	10½
	Do. 9-ft. do. do. "	1	1½
	Do. 10-ft. do. do. "	1	2
15.	Cutting Holes through Ribs per hole up to one yard thick. Over 3-ft. heading price or bord, as the case may be	2	6
16.	Setting and Sawing Soft Wood Chocks to be done by the day.		
17.	Wherever a Chain is used up the face up to 20 yards long... ... ... per dozen	0	6
18.	Tramming Timber into "Benks or Posts" "	0	1
19.	Jinnying and Jutting in "Benks or Posts" "	0	6
20.	Jutting only in "Benks or Posts" "	0	4
21.	Filling uphill in "Posts" ... ... "	0	6

		s.	d.
22.	Taking out Bars down Gate Roads ... per bar	0	4
	Taking out Props down Gate Road ...per prop	0	1
23.	Tramming Rises, first Rise due after 77 yards, and 2½d. per dozen for every 20 yards after 77.		
24.	Tramming through doors ... ... per dozen	0	1
25.	Colliers working by the day ... ... per day	5	0
26.	Trammers working by the day ... ... "	4	0
27.	Filling Water into barrels ... per barrel	0	3
28.	Filling Dirt ... ... per tub	0	3
29.	Emptying Dirt ... ... "	0	3
	(If emptied into packs, packing price to cover emptying)		
30.	Cutting Bags in Gates or Wastes ... per yard	0	6
31.	Lomping up to 30 yards ... ... per dozen	1	0
32.	Laying Round Turns ... ... each	1	6
33.	Laying Square Turns - First time ... "	2	0
34.	Laying Square Turns After first time ... "	1	0
35.	Laying Flat Sheets ... ... each time	0	6
36.	Tramming Chocks into "Benks or Posts" per chock	0	3
37.	Finishing Working Places... ... for job	5	0
38.	Working in Wet Places in Headings ...per yard	0	6
39.	Making Refuge Holes "End of Bord,"3 yds. for 2 yds.		
40.	For pulling Rails up in places finishing ... per pair	0	0½
41.	Hard and Difficult Places to be arranged for between Manager and Men concerned.		
42.	Opening out alongside Old Levels ... per yard	2	11½
43.	Where two Colliers and two Trammers are working together and at either side of Gate per dozen	0	2
	District Percentages to be added to above.		

Signed on behalf of Messrs. J. & J. Charlesworth, Limited.

J. STOBART CHARLESWORTH · W. G. CHARLESWORTH
SAMUEL MELLORS (Manager).

Signed on behalf of the men,

MOSES HARTLEY · CHAS. COOPER · TOM RAMSDEN
JAMES HADDOCK · JOSEPH ELLIS · JAS. H. PICKERSGILL
JACOB SMITH · ARTHUR THORPE · FRANCIS MOTTASHED

November 27th, 1906.

A Kilnhurst & Thrybergh Hall Collieries list, of 1906, of prices paid to men for particular work as agreed between the colliery owners and management and the workmen's representatives.

Warncliffe Silkstone Colliery was sunk to work the Silkstone seam of coal from 1853 initially, under the aegis of the Great Northern Railway Co. It came under the ownership of a limited liabilty company from 1879 and to possess access to a number of rival mainline railways and had 1,415 employees in 1897, 1,527 in 1918. It finally closed in 1967.

Wharncliffe Silkstone Colliery: a view published in 1924.

Wharncliffe Silkstone colliers' housing – unusual in South Yorkshire by being small and single storeyed.

Another view of the Wharncliffe Silkstone single-storey cottages, which had bedrooms in the roofspace, taken in 1960 with the colliery spoilheap rising behind.

Wharncliffe Silkstone had colliery baths opened around 1892 and shown here, unused, in 1960.

The Wharncliffe Silkstone colliery school of about 1892, attached to the bath block, in 1960.

George Blake Walker, 'Mr Wharncliffe Silkstone.' He was educated in colliery work on Tyneside, was responsible at Wharncliffe Silkstone Colliery for the highly successful development of thin seams – introducing coal cutters and conveyors – and was involved in the establishment of the first Yorkshire Coalfield Mines Rescue Station, opened at Tankersley in 1902.

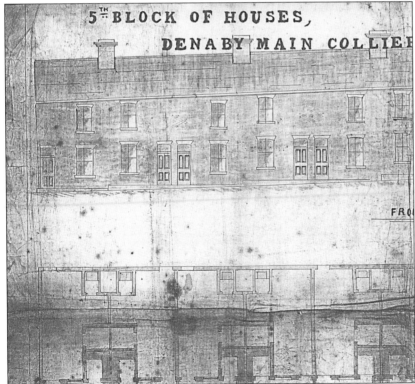

5ᵀᴴ BLOCK OF HOUSES, DENABY MAIN COLLIER

More typical South Yorkshire colliery workers' housing: plans for cottages at Denaby Main Colliery, c.1860.

Monckton Main Colliery had its first shaft sod cut in mid-1875 and reached the Barnsley seam at 477 yards. It had immediate access to mainline railways and to the adjacent and modernised Barnsley Canal and worked under both large and small freeholders' estates. The Royston Drift opened here in 1976 and the colliery closed in 1989.

ALL COMMUNICATIONS TO BE ADDRESSED TO THE FIRM.

SHIPPING PORTS:
JLL, GRIMSBY, GOOLE &
KEADBY.

TELEGRAMS.
"MONCKTON, BARNSLEY."

Telephone
Nº 1 POST OFFICE,
BARNSLEY.

IN DIRECT COMMUNICATIO
WITH THE
MIDLAND GT CENTRAL AND
& BARNSLEY RAILWA
AND THE
AIRE & CALDER CAN

COKE & BRICK MANUFACTURERS,

THE MONCKTON MAIN COAL Cº LIMP.

NEAR BARNSLEY   22nd March 1901

Monckton Main Colliery illustrated letterhead of the 1890s referring to the Great Central Railway.

Monckton Main Colliery, an undated postcard showing railway waggons with pre-1923 amalgamation naming.

Monckton Main view, posted after 1910.

Rear view of Monckton Main.

A new winding engine under construction at Monckton Main.

The new winding engine completed.

Monckton Main's pit yard.

The coke oven at Monckton Main.

The underground stables at Monckton

A new dynamo at Monckton Main.

The lamp room.

The screens at Monckton Main.

The feeder tramway from an auxiliary colliery.

Sinkers standing above the sinking hoppit.

The laboratory for the colliery and the coke works.

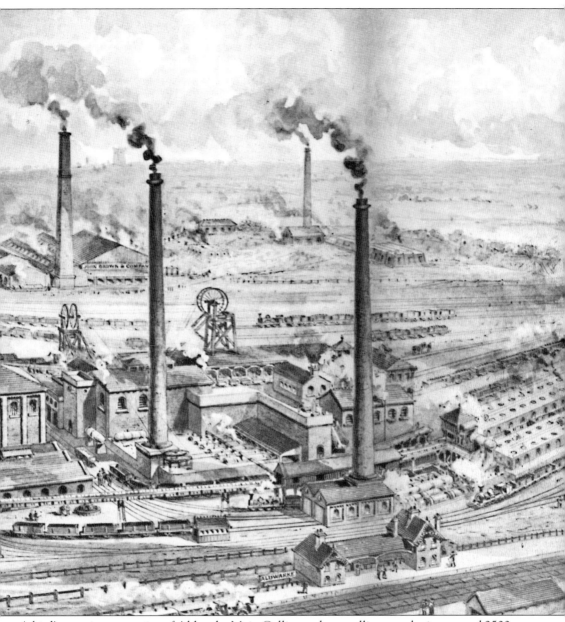

A bird's eye view engraving of Aldwarke Main Colliery, a large colliery employing around 2500, c.1880.

Old Silkstone colliery, Dodworth. There is a reference to coal working at Silkstone in 1293, and the working of the excellent quality 6ft thick Silkstone seam appears to have continued on a small scale. Some industrialisation in the area, new technologies and the advent of proposals for canals which would reduce coal transport costs and hence open much wider markets, may have been the occasion for advertisements for coal to let at Silkstone in the later 1780s. However, the canal did not reach the district until 1802, and the coal trade only developed slowly until the opening of the canal company's Silkstone Railway in 1809.

By the 1820s one colliery owner at Silkstone was sending coal via the distant Ouse, Foss, Ure and Derwent navigations in Yorkshire, and on the first day of 1850 the Silkstone branch railway opened, allowing access to even wider markets.

The area saw many independent collieries come and go, both large and small, long and short lived, until the closure of Redbrook Colliery in 1987. The Silkstone Four Foot seam, of much lower quality as well as thickness, was extensively worked by small mines in the twentieth century, and much opencast mining has taken place in the area as well.

Above, below, and opposite: Parts of the Old Silkstone Collieries empire from pictures published in 1924.

Woolley Colliery was, for many decades, essentially a drift mine, albeit one on a large scale. Sunk in an area where coal mining had occurred on a small scale for some centuries – since at least 1301 – the new colliery opened in 1854. It adjoined the new Barnsley branch railway, only opened itself in 1850, but which now provided facilities for coal sales in an area much wider than the vicinity of Woolley and Darton, or indeed of the West Riding. The outcrop of the Barnsley seam was followed from close to the new railway line to the dip – downhill – which created difficulties with regard to pumping water and bringing coal to the surface.

In 1861 a disastrous influx of water had to be contended with and money for development became short. There were labour troubles, the costs of cottage building and day-school maintenance had to be met and no signs of the colliery were to intrude upon the view from Woolley Hall, the coal lessor's mansion. A joint stock company was established in 1867 to provide new finance, and in 1873, at the height of the coal boom, the colliery was sold. The principal partner of the new company was George Pearson of Pontefract, a retired railway contractor who was also a partner in West Riding, Denaby Main and Darfield Main collieries.

In 1896 the colliery was transferred to the ownership of the Fountain & Burnley partnership, which owned North Gawber Colliery nearby. In 1910 work was begun on sinking shafts to seams below the Barnsley seam; it employed 1,215 men and boys by 1922. It survived nationalisation and was the stamping ground of Arthur Scargill as he rose in the union hierarchy. It only closed in 1987.

South Kirkby Colliery, sunk in what was described initially as 'terra incognita' in coal terms, was worked under a lease from 1874 of 1,700 acres of coal by the Rosedale & Ferryhill Iron Co. That particular company failed in 1879 and a new company was established in 1880 and the Barnsley seam worked from 1883. By 1897 it employed 901 people and 2,283 by 1918. It finally closed in 1988.

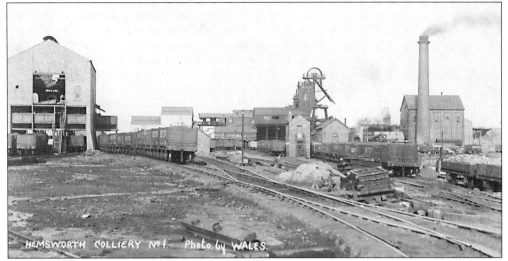

Hemsworth Colliery (also known as Hemsworth Fitzwilliam). The opening of the West Riding & Grimsby Railway in 1866, across a tract of country where the Barnsley Bed of coal was unproved, led to exploratory borings in 1869 which indeed proved the existence of that seam at 612 yards. Richard and George A. Fosdick, London coal merchants, sank a new colliery in this agricultural area, which opened in 1876 in the period of the Great Depression. Richard Fosdick's venture failed in 1879, having accrued debts of £100,000, with nearly 300 men and boys employed. The colliery was maintained by a liquidator and worked until a new company was formed in 1890. Output rose from the 180,000 tons of 1889 to 300,000 tons a decade later. However, the new company was relatively unsuccessful too.

In 1905, during yet another change of ownership, the well documented evictions of workers and their families occurred. The colliery closed in 1967, upon merging with South Kirkby.

Above and overleaf: Rare photographs of underground workings in the pits of the Hemsworth and South Kirkby collieries, published in 1913.

Hemsworth and South Kirkby underground: Setting & removing props.

The seven men killed in the Barrow Colliery cage fall disaster of 1907.

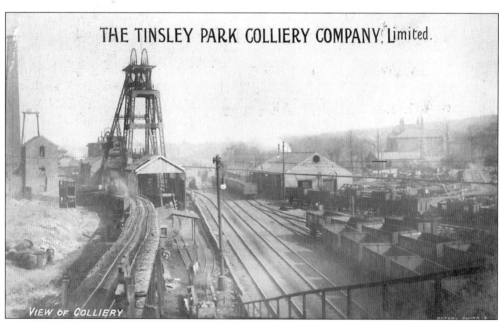

Tinsley Park Colliery, near Sheffield. Claimed to have been sunk in 1842, the Tinsley Park Co., working on the edge of Sheffield, had 121 workers in 1897, which had enlarged to 1,610 in 1913. It closed during the Second World War, just before nationalisation.

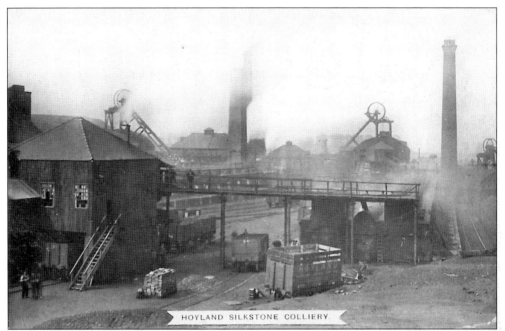

HOYLAND SILKSTONE COLLIERY.

Hoyland Silkstone Colliery was the first where proposals were made to sink to the Silkstone seam, below the Barnsley Bed. Lease negotiations were begun in 1871 and the coal won early in 1876. It was one of several South Yorkshire collieries which were at various times offered for sale by auction; it was purchased. by Newton, Chambers & Co., the ironmasters, who also sank the nearby Rockingham Colliery.

Newton, Chambers & Co. was established in 1793, and soon developed its own coke-fired blast furnace production of iron, using local ores. An engraving of the works was published in a trade directory of 1825 and shows a waggonway and colliery/ironpit steam engines in the background, as well as the works.

FRANCIS CHANDLER.

The first man to receive King Edward's Medal, which is equivalent to the Victoria Cross.

The Medal was given to Mr. F. Chandler, by the King, on February 27th, 1908, for the heroic efforts he made to save his fellow workmen in the Pit Disaster at the Hoyland Silkstone Colliery, near Barnsley.

Quo fas et gloria ducunt.

The Hoyland Silkstone hero, Francis Chandler.

93

The North Gawber Colliery fitting shops. North Gawber Colliery was sunk under a lease of 1853 in an area where coal mining had featured since at least 1423. The sinking only became economically viable as a result of the new coal markets proffered by the nearby Barnsley branch railway of the Lancashire & Yorkshire Railway Co. The lease was taken in 1853 by two brothers Thorp, sons of Samuel Thorp, coalmaster and of the family which originated the modern Barnsley coal industry from the 1770s; their older Barnsley Bed collieries were working out nearer to the outcrop. The colliery was shallow – only 108 yards to the Barnsley seam – but it was economically successful.

It was sold in 1872, following the deaths of active Thorp partners, to a new company which found the onset of the coal depression impossible to overcome. It was sold again – by auction, and the sale particulars survive – in 1885, to the firm of Fountain & Burnley, which had long established coal mining interests nearby, and which was to buy Woolley Colliery in 1896. Sinkings were subsequently made to deeper seams.

Rotherham Main Colliery, at Canklow, was sunk in 1890-1893 and closed in 1954. In 1911 it employed 2,388 men and boys.

Hickleton Main Colliery was sunk in 1892-1894 by a Sheffield-financed company, and the Barnsley Bed was reached and won in June 1894. By 1918 there were 2,110 employees and in 1922 annual output was 1.2 million tons. The colliery closed in 1986, having been merged with nearby Goldthorpe/Highgate.

Hickleton Main once more in a 1913 postcard.

Grimethorpe Colliery.

Grimethorpe Colliery, *c*.1900. The coal here – the Barnsley Bed – was reached in 1897 and became yet another large colliery, employing 2,608 men and boys in 1911.

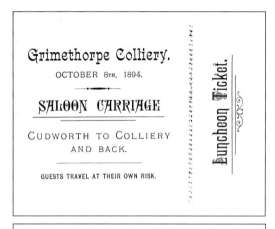

Grimethorpe Colliery.

OCTOBER 8TH, 1894.

SALOON CARRIAGE

CUDWORTH TO COLLIERY AND BACK.

GUESTS TRAVEL AT THEIR OWN RISK.

Luncheon Ticket.

The Directors of the Mitchell Main Colliery Co. Limited request the honour of the company of

on the occasion of the turning of the First Sod of their new
Grimethorpe Colliery,
on Monday, October 8th 1894 at 1.30 p.m.
and to Luncheon afterwards.
The favour of an immediate reply will oblige.
Conveyances will be at Cudworth Station at 1.15 p.m.

PLEASE ADDRESS REPLY TO { J. W. H. Mitchell SECRETARY
Regent St.
Barnsley

Some details of the considerable ceremony for the cutting of the first sod of the Grimethorpe colliery for the Carlton Main Colliery Co. Ltd in October 1894.

Turning of the First Sod at the

NEW GRIMETHORPE COLLIERY.

LUNCHEON,

OCTOBER 8TH, 1894.

WINE LIST.

CHAMPAGNE.

George Goulet's Extra Quality Dry, 1887 Vintage.

Jules Pommett et Fils Extra Quality Dry,
1887 Vintage.

Theophile Roederer & Co., Extra Reserve Cuvee,
1884 Vintage.

SHERRY.

Very Fine Manzanilla, Bottled 1806.

Fine Old Pale, 1868 Vintage.

CLARET.

Chateau Grand Puy Lacoste.   S. Julien.

HOCK.

Nierstein and Marcobrunn.

Very Fine Old Cognac, Denis Mounie's
1878 Vintage.

Very Fine Old Highland Blend of Scotch Whisky.

GEORGE HORNE,
Wine Merchant, Barnsley.

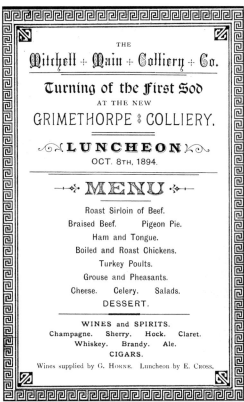

THE

Mitchell + Main + Colliery + Co.

Turning of the First Sod

AT THE NEW

GRIMETHORPE COLLIERY.

LUNCHEON

OCT. 8TH, 1894.

MENU

Roast Sirloin of Beef.

Braised Beef.   Pigeon Pie.

Ham and Tongue.

Boiled and Roast Chickens.

Turkey Poults.

Grouse and Pheasants.

Cheese.   Celery.   Salads.

DESSERT.

WINES and SPIRITS.

Champagne.   Sherry.   Hock.   Claret.

Whiskey.   Brandy.   Ale.

CIGARS.

Wines supplied by G. Horne.   Luncheon by E. Cross.

A sumptious luncheon was provided for the occasion.

Wharncliffe Carlton Colliery was a new, adjoining colliery belonging to East Gawber Hall, worked largely under the Carlton estate of the Earls of Wharncliffe.

In Affectionate Remembrance of

TWENTY COLLIERS,

Whose lives were sacrifised in the Explosion at Wharncliffe Carlton Pit, October 17th, 1883.

James Flatney,	aged 14 Yrs.	John Hallam,	aged 41 Yrs.
George Mason,	,, 16 ,,	John Wright,	,, 46 ,,
George Phillips,	,, 19 ,,	William Lawson,	,, 49 ,,
Fredk. Holland,	,, 25 ,,	Richard Garbutt,	,, 49 ,,
Edward Weller,	,, 28 ,,	Charles Phillips,	,, 54 ,,
Albert Button,	,, 32 ,,	William Shaw,	,, 54 ,,
Charles Starkey,	,, 36 ,,	Henry Fisher,	,, 54 ,,
William Goulding	,, 40 ,,	Thomas Wood,	,, 55 ,,
William Mason,	,, 40 ,,	Ellis Ambler,	,, 58 ,,
William Fisher,	,, 41 ,,	George Egley,	,, 65 ,,

God grant that all who weep, O'er loved ones from us riven;
Unbroken families may meet, Around the throne of heaven.

Cards commemorating the dead in the Wharncliffe-Carlton disaster of 1883.

In Affectionate Remembrance of

JABEZ REDHALL,

The beloved Son of Rebecca Redhall,

WHO WAS KILLED AT EAST GAWBER COLLIERY, SEPT. 8th, 1887,

AGED 20 YEARS,

And was Interred at Barnsley Cemetery, September 11th.

When I left home I little thought, My time was so near run; But ah! the Lord he called on me, Ere that day's work was done.	Sudden was the death of me, A great surprise to all: When the Lord thought fit I must obey I could not refuse his call.

A fine commercial photograph of Hoyland Silkstone Colliery in the 1890s.

TANKERSLEY PIT

Tankersley Colliery at the time of the riots of 1870.

Monk Bretton Colliery was one of the first to be sunk to the Barnsley Bed between Barnsley and Wakefield, as that seam's workable coal neared exhaustion close to Barnsley itself. Increased competition between railway companies and the flourishing, independently-owned Barnsley Canal nearby were the catalysts for the venture, and the colliery's first sod (for shaft sinking) was cut in May 1867, the coal being won at 300 yards in July 1870.

The promoter of the colliery was William Pepper, son of a retired Monk Bretton bleacher and minor landowner, although Pepper himself was a railway servant. He brought into partnership William Day, owner of large, Barnsley Bed collieries that were nearing exhaustion, and T.M. Carter, a Wakefield brewer and also a colliery owner, with T.W. Embleton, senior, the long-serving manager of the great Middleton Colliery near Leeds. The new colliery's coals were used for railway companies' fastest expresses, for steam fishing trawlers and for iron making at home and abroad. Even the London market recognised that this part of the seam provided the best house coal.

Monk Bretton closed in 1968, with 889 employees. The illustrations used here are from the colliery's publicity booklet (without date), reprinted from *The Gentleman's Journal & Gentlewoman's Court Review.*

Another Monkbretton Colliery scene, *c.*1900

100

Barnsley Main's no. 2 pit, which employed 1,421 in 1911, and its coking plant from views published in 1913.

Scenes of the pitheads of Barnsley Main Colliery published in 1913. The colliery had a complex history, closing and re-opening on several occasions, with final closure occurring in 1991.

Following page: Frickley Colliery marked the advance of coal working eastwards toward the Doncaster. Sinking began in March 1903 and the Barnsley seam was reached in May 1905. The first coal left the colliery in September 1905. As was so frequently the case, rents from the working of coal enriched the local landowning Warde Aldam family of Frickley Hall and utmost care was taken to minimise disruption to the estate.

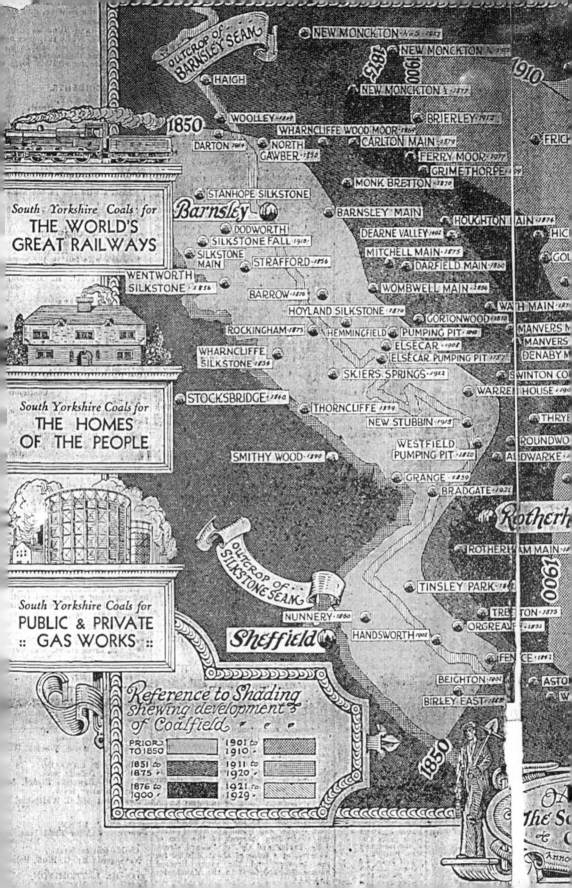

OUTCROP OF BARNSLEY SEAM

1875
1900
1910

NEW MONCKTON No 5 1927
NEW MONCKTON No 1911
NEW MONCKTON ½ 1877
BRIERLEY 1912
FRICK

HAIGH

1850
WOOLLEY 1869
WHARNCLIFFE WOOD MOOR 1869
CARLTON MAIN 1879
FERRY MOOR 1977
GRIMETHORPE 1899
DARTON 1914
NORTH GAWBER 1850
MONK BRETTON 1870
HIC

STANHOPE SILKSTONE
BARNSLEY MAIN
HOUGHTON MAIN 1874
HIC

Barnsley
DODWORTH
DEARNE VALLEY 1902
GOU

SILKSTONE FALL 1913
MITCHELL MAIN 1875
SILKSTONE MAIN
STRAFFORD 1856
DARFIELD MAIN 1860

WENTWORTH SILKSTONE 1856
WOMBWELL MAIN 1856

WATH MAIN

BARROW 1876
HOYLAND SILKSTONE 1870
GORTONWOOD 1875
MANVERS M

ROCKINGHAM 1875
HEMMINGFIELD
PUMPING PIT 1910
MANVERS M

WHARNCLIFFE SILKSTONE 1854
ELSECAR 1908
DENABY M

ELSECAR PUMPING PIT 1787
SWINTON CO

SKIERS SPRINGS 1922
WARREN HOUSE

STOCKSBRIDGE 1860
THRYB

THORNCLIFFE 1359
NEW STUBBIN 1913
ROUNDWO

WESTFIELD PUMPING PIT 1820
ALDWARKE

SMITHY WOOD 1899

GRANGE 1859
BRADGATE 1921

OUTCROP OF SILKSTONE SEAM

Rotherh

ROTHERHAM MAIN

1900

TINSLEY PARK 1865
TREETON 1875

NUNNERY 1860
ORGREAVE 1851

Sheffield
HANDSWORTH 1902
FENCE 1892

BEIGHTON 1904
ASTO

BIRLEY EAST 1888
W

1850

Reference to Shading
shewing development
of Coalfield

PRIOR TO 1850		1901 to 1910	
1851 to 1875		1911 to 1920	
1876 to 1900		1921 to 1929	

A
The Se

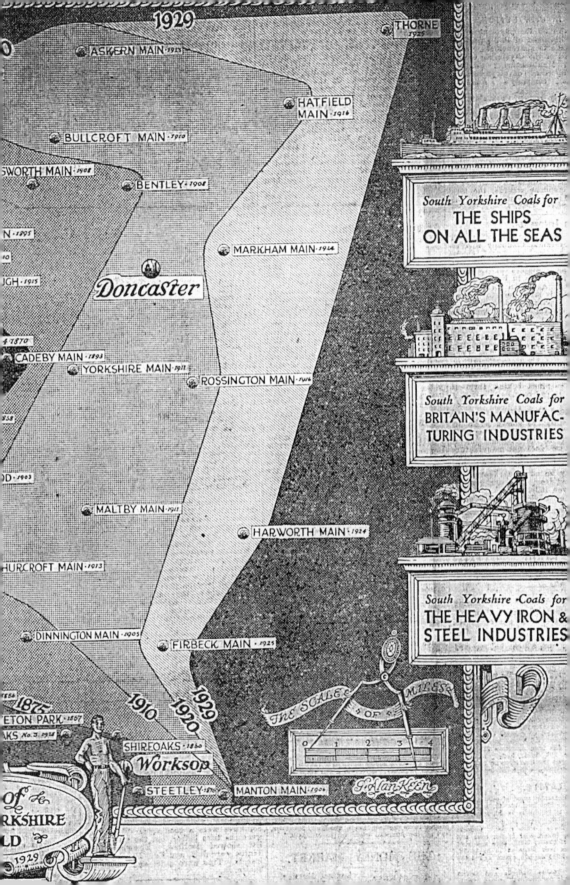

1929

THORNE 1925

ASKERN MAIN 1913

BULLCROFT MAIN 1910

...SWORTH MAIN 1908

HATFIELD MAIN 1916

BENTLEY 1908

...N 1895

...JGH 1915

Doncaster

MARKHAM MAIN 1914

...4 1870

CADEBY MAIN 1893

YORKSHIRE MAIN 1911

ROSSINGTON MAIN 1916

...858

...0D 1903

MALTBY MAIN 1911

HARWORTH MAIN 1924

...HURCROFT MAIN 1913

DINNINGTON MAIN 1905

FIRBECK MAIN 1925

1910 1920 1929

...1875

...ETON PARK 1867

...AKS No.3 1914

SHIREOAKS 1860

Worksop

STEETLEY 1876 MANTON MAIN 1906

South Yorkshire Coals for
THE SHIPS ON ALL THE SEAS

South Yorkshire Coals for
BRITAIN'S MANUFAC-TURING INDUSTRIES

South Yorkshire Coals for
THE HEAVY IRON & STEEL INDUSTRIES

THE SCALE OF MILES
0 1 2 3 4

Roy Van Keen

...OF...
...RKSHIRE
...LD
1929

Bentley Colliery, sunk in a rural area just outside Doncaster between 1905 and 1909.

Three
At and Around Doncaster

A postcard of Bentley Colliery posted in 1909. Although the Doncaster area only began to develop its coal resources in the early twentieth century, there were earlier efforts to prove the presence of coal and to exploit it. In 1835 a borehole was put down at Reedness, near Goole, reaching 343 yards, but no coal was found. Much later, in 1874, Sir W.R. Cooke leased his coal at Arksey, Bentley and Wheatley to a County Durham colliery owner and, in 1888, an announcement was made that a sinking was to occur at Bentley. However, it was not until the middle of the first decade of the twentieth century that collieries close to Doncaster were actually opened.

Bullcroft Main Colliery at Carcroft, near Doncaster, was sunk in 1909-1911. It closed in 1970 on merging with Brodsworth. Note the temporary wooden headstocks

Askern Main, which adjoined a small and picturesque spa village, was sunk in 1911-1916.

Rossington Main Colliery was sunk in 1912-1915 to the Barnsley Bed at 873 yards.

The sinking of Thorne Colliery was begun in 1909 but not completed until 1911. It had a chequered career and closed in 1956 for major shaft repairs.

Maltby Main Colliery, sunk in 1907 to 1910, employed 478 in 1911.

Another Maltby Main view from a card posted in 1911.

Goldthorpe Colliery, from a postcard sent in 1929. The colliery worked an area where coalmining had featured since 1678. A rural colliery, with a steam pumping engine, situated close to a turnpike road, was in existence by 1770, yet had closed by 1783. The new colliery was opened in 1909-1910 by Henry Lodge & Co.

Colliers' workings opened in Warren Quarry Lane, Barnsley, during the coal strike of 1912.

A 1930s aerial view of Brodsworth Main Colliery.

Brodsworth Main Colliery was promoted as a separate concern by the Hickleton and Staveley companies with a huge capital outlay of £300,000 to work 6,000 acres under the Brodsworth Hall estate of the Thellusson family. The first sod was cut in 1905 and the Barnsley seam reached just two years later – at 300 yards, less depth than had been anticipated – and coal was produced a year later. It was necessary to construct a colliery village, replete with ancillary sevices, and a 'model village' was built, connected to the neighbouring market town of Doncaster by an electric tramway. Brodsworth employed 2,004 by 1914 and closed in 1990.

Above and following pages: Yorkshire Main Colliery, at New Edlington near Doncaster, reached the Barnsley Bed seam at 905 yards from the surface in June 1911. Sinking only took a total of eighteen months.

Again, it was necessary to provide a model village and all associated structures – even an open air swimming bath.

Yorkshire Main: Erecting the
Headstocks

Yorkshire Main: A twin level cage

The rescue team.

BRADEWORTH MAIN COLLIERY AMBULANCE

An underground roadway junction

The sports ground

The pit fire brigade.

KING AND QUEEN'S VISIT TO WOODLANDS VILLAGE JULY 9TH 1912

Brodsworth Main Colliery's model village.

Above and on the following pages: Yorkshire Main Colliery

Headgear and a winding engine.

A winding engine in its long shed.

Full and empty tubs.

The coal washer.

Creating a spoil heap.

The concert hall.

Good quality housing.

The swimming pool.

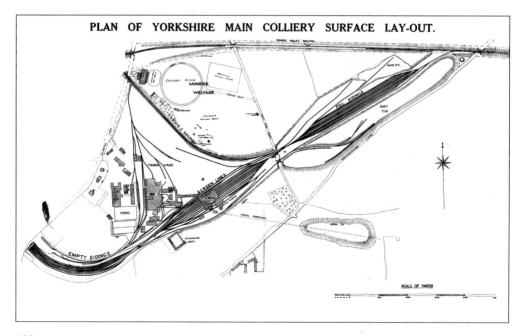

PLAN OF YORKSHIRE MAIN COLLIERY SURFACE LAY-OUT.

YORKSHIRE MAIN COLLIERY UNDERGROUND LAY-OUT.

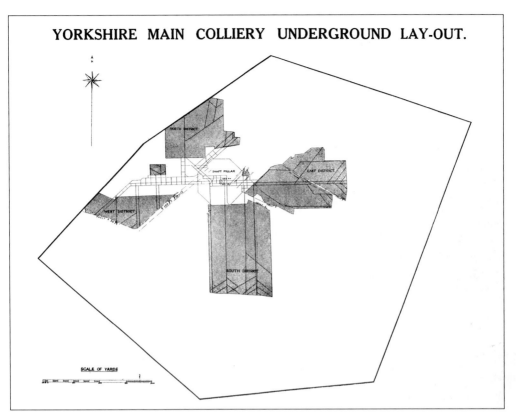

The end of an era. Wombwell Main men wear black armbands as they carry their Lodge banner for the last time in the Miner's gala of 1969. Their march is led by Roy Hepworth, who lost a leg in a colliery accident.

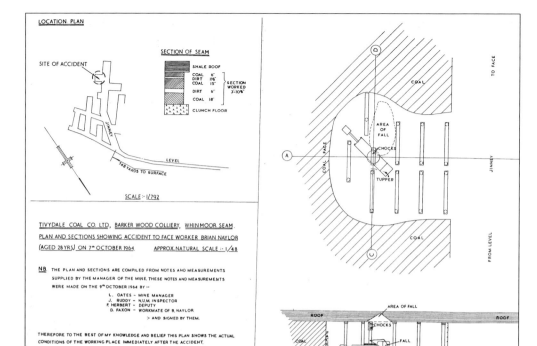

LOCATION PLAN

SECTION OF SEAM

SITE OF ACCIDENT

SHALE ROOF

COAL	6"
DIRT	1½"
COAL	15"
DIRT	6"
COAL	18"

SECTION WORKED 3'-10½"

CLUNCH FLOOR

JINNEY

LEVEL

748 YARDS TO SURFACE

SCALE :- 1/792

TIVYDALE COAL CO LTD, BARKER WOOD COLLIERY, WHINMOOR SEAM.
PLAN AND SECTIONS SHOWING ACCIDENT TO FACE WORKER BRIAN NAYLOR
(AGED 28 YRS) ON 7ᵗʰ OCTOBER 1964.   APPROX. NATURAL SCALE :- 1/48

NB. THE PLAN AND SECTIONS ARE COMPILED FROM NOTES AND MEASUREMENTS
SUPPLIED BY THE MANAGER OF THE MINE. THESE NOTES AND MEASUREMENTS
WERE MADE ON THE 9ᵗʰ OCTOBER 1964 BY :-

L. OATES - MINE MANAGER
J. RUDDY - N.U.M. INSPECTOR
F. HERBERT - DEPUTY
D. FAXON - WORKMATE OF B. NAYLOR
> AND SIGNED BY THEM.

THEREFORE TO THE BEST OF MY KNOWLEDGE AND BELIEF THIS PLAN SHOWS THE ACTUAL
CONDITIONS OF THE WORKING PLACE IMMEDIATELY AFTER THE ACCIDENT.

SIGNED [signature] 14/10/1964

G.E. SKEITH (SURVEYOR) MAKER OF THIS PLAN

TO FACE
COAL
AREA OF FALL
CHOCKS
TUPPER
JINNEY
FROM LEVEL
COAL FACE
A
C

AREA OF FALL
ROOF   ROOF
CHOCKS
COAL   FACE   FALL
A   FLOOR   JINNEY
FALLING GRADIENT 1 IN 66

SECTION ALONG LINE A-B

Midland Railway Company.

The Committees of the

MANVERS MAIN COLLIERIES,

Underground and Surface Workmen, have pleasure in announcing to the Workmen that they have made arrangements with the above Company to run their

ANNUAL EXCURSION

TO

SOUTHPORT

For 1, 3 or 5 Days,

On Saturday, July 12th, 1890.

STATIONS AND TIMES OF STARTING.		FARES THERE AND BACK.	
		1 DAY.	3 or 5 DAYS.
SWINTON	4·25 4·35	**3s. 6d.**	**5s. 6d.**
WATH	4·31 4·41		

Children under 12 Half-fare.

The Return Trains will leave Southport at 7·55 o'clock and 8·10 p.m. same day.   Long Date Passengers return by any ordinary train.

Tickets will be available by this Train only.

Workmen's Tickets may be had from Messrs. Simms, Critchley, Venables, Mansell, Lawrence, and Getting, at each Lodge House on producing their Union Card, from 4 o'clock till 8 p.m., at 2s. 6d. each; Boys working at the Colliery, 1s. 3d.   No Workman will be supplied with more than two Tickets at reduced rate; Boys, one.   Tickets to be sold on Friday night only at reduced rate.   All Tickets sold on Saturday morning will be charged for at the rate of 3s. 6d. each, by Messrs· Thomas Flatters, Schofield Street, Mexboro', and Frank Jeavons, Winterwell, to whom the General Public must apply.

LONG-DATE TICKETS TO BE HAD AT THE STATIONS.

Walter Turner, Printer, High Street, Mexboro' (National Telephone, No. 1506.)

Barker Wood Colliery: an accident plan of 1964 relating to a small mine near Silkstone, one of those excluded from nationalisation owing to the small size of its workforce. Part of the Whinmoor seams are shown.

A colliery trip to the seaside in 1890.

Order of (inter-denominational) Service at the burial of those killed in the Bentley Colliery disaster of 1931.

Rossington – known as New Rossington – colliery village's layout plan of the 1920s.

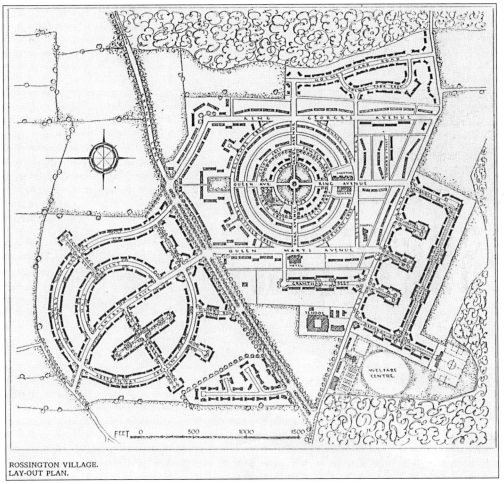

ROSSINGTON VILLAGE.
LAY-OUT PLAN.

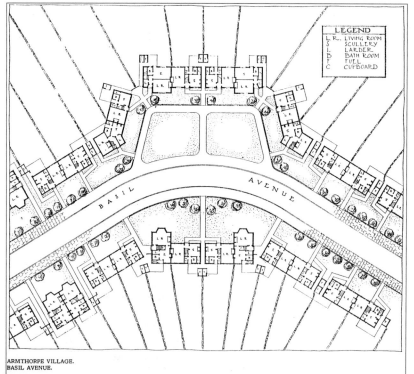

Armthorpe colliery village, showing the internal arrangements of 'model' housing in the 1920s.

ARMTHORPE VILLAGE.
BASIL AVENUE.

WOODLANDS VILLAGE.
GREAT NORTH ROAD.

Woodlands village – housing for Brodsworth Main Colliery – alongside the Great North Road, with a tramcar approaching the village in the 1920s.

126

Technological advance in the 1790s: John Curr of Sheffield's guide for colliery owners and managers of 1796-1797.

THE

COAL VIEWER,

AND

ENGINE BUILDER's

PRACTICAL

COMPANION.

BY JOHN CURR, OF SHEFFIELD.

SHEFFIELD:

PRINTED FOR THE Author, BY JOHN NORTHALL.

And Sold by
I. & J. TAYLOR, *at the* ARCHITECTURAL LIBRARY, HIGH HOLBORN, *London*; JOSEPH WHITFIELD, *Newcastle-upon-Tyne*; ARCHIBALD CONSTABLE, *Edinburgh*; DUNLOP & WILSON, *Glasgow*; I. & W. EDDOWES, *Shrewsbury*; AND JAMES HARROP, *Manchester*.

ENTERED *at* STATIONER's HALL.

1797.

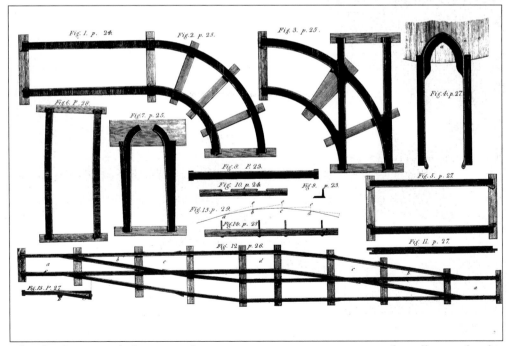

John Curr's tramroad plates: a modern improvement in transporting coal, as illustrated in his book of 1797.

Souvenir In Affectionate Rememberance

OF THE

MEN WHO LOST THEIR LIVES IN THE
MALTBY MAIN COLLIERY DISASTER

SATURDAY 28th JULY 1923.

"IN THE MIDST OF LIFE WE ARE IN DEATH"

JOHN STOKER, Age 30, overman, McLaven-crescent
HARRY NORWOOD, Age 30, 5 Victoria-street
GEORGE PERRINS, Age 38, 186 Muglet-lane
ERNEST CLIXBY, Age 27, chemist 64 Church-road Darnall
BERT BEARDSLEY Age 29, 13 King's Avenue
HAROLD BOURNE, Age 25, 49 Salisbury-place
GEORGE BRIERLBY Age 34, Victory-street
RICHARD JOHN BROOKS, Age 24 6 Coleridge-road
AARON DANIELS, Age 46, 13 Coleridge-road
ERNEST DUNN, Age 28, 3 Grange-lane
WILLIAM EMBERTON, Age 28, 39 Salisbury-road
JOHN HENRY GARRATTY, Age 38, 56 Muglet-lane
G. HICKLING, Age 47, 128 Tickhill-road

BENJAMIN JONES Age 27, 103 Salisbury-road
L. MEREDITH, Age 23, 26 Beresford-road
WILLIAM PRIEST, Age 25 8 Carlisle-road
JAMES SMITH, Age 35, 5 Scarbrough-crescent
ALBERT SMITHSON, Age 29, King's-avenue
JOSEPH SPIBEY Age 29, 6 Salisbury-road
JONATHAN SPILSBURY, Age 30, 4 Cavendish-place
SYLVANUS TURNER. Age 28, 12 Beresford-road
JOSEPH BEST, Age 19, 3 Deacons-crescent
RAYMOND C. BOURNE, Age 19, 4 Salisbury-place
ALFRED LESLIE FELLOWS, Age 15, Tennyson-rd
J. GREEN, Age 33, 78 Nelson-road
E. T. MITCHELL, Age 23, 56 Atholstone-rd Conisboro
R. RENSHAW, Age 48 road layer, 14 Farquhar-road

A sudden change dear friends upon us fell
Wehad no time to bid you all farewell
Think nothing strange death happens unto all
Our lots to-day, to-morrow yours may fall

Do not ask us if we miss them
There is such a vacant place
We cannot forget their footsteps
And their dear familiar face.

Printer S. Burgess, 8 York Place Strand London, W.C.2,

The price of coal: the Maltby Main Colliery disaster of 1923. Details and verse on a paper hand-kerchief.